Nursing Homes

LINDA HORN AND ELMA GRIESEL

introduction by Maggie Kuhn

nursing homes
a citizens'
action
guide

BEACON PRESS BOSTON

Copyright © 1977 by Linda Horn and Elma Griesel

Beacon Press books are published under the auspices
of the Unitarian Universalist Association

Published simultaneously in hardcover and paperback editions

Simultaneous publication in Canada
by Fitzhenry & Whiteside, Ltd., Toronto

Printed in the United States of America

(hardcover) 9 8 7 6 5 4 3 2 1
(paperback) 9 8 7 6 5 4 3 2

Library of Congress Cataloging in Publication Data

Horn, Linda.
    Nursing homes.
    Bibliography: p.
    1. Nursing homes — United States.   2. Nursing homes —
United States — Administration — Citizen participation.
I. Griesel, Elma, joint author.   II. Title
RA997.H67 362.6'15'0973   75-7745
ISBN 0-8070-0870-2
ISBN 0-8070-0871-1 (pbk.)

To Pat Powers . . .
To Florence . . .
To our families and friends . . .
To the residents of nursing homes.

CONTENTS

ACKNOWLEDGMENTS

This book could not have been written without the support and assistance of many friends and dedicated citizen activists.

We are extremely grateful to the citizen action groups and the individuals described herein, many of whom spent a great deal of time preparing materials for us.

We sincerely acknowledge the Women's Program of the United Presbyterian Church, whose grant to the Gray Panthers made possible the research for this book.

We are indebted to Dr. Matilda Moore, who introduced Beacon Press to us, and to Mr. Ray Bentley, our editor, who has been kind, tolerant, and so patient.

We extend our heartfelt thanks to all the people who have contributed in various ways to research, support, and help shape this book through interviews, thoughtful comments, ideas, and discussions.

Peg Thornhill provided editorial and proofreading assistance and encouragement when it was greatly needed. Friend and consultant Patricia Powers helped in writing the legislative lobbying section. Georgia Mathis Springer provided assistance with the legal resources section. We thank Senator Frank Moss, Chairman, and Val Halamandaris, Associate Counsel, U.S. Senate Subcommittee on Long-Term Care, for their efforts to encourage reform. We acknowledge Ralph Nader and his workers, for the Gray Panther project is an outgrowth of Nader's Study Group Report on nursing homes and the activities of the Retired Professional Action Group.

Special assistance and support have also been provided by June Lewis, Ann Wyatt, Jean Hopper, Carol Hyde, Violet Bemmels, and Bobbi Granger.

We have recognized and do acknowledge those nursing home owners, administrators, and staff of exemplary institutions, who through their examples have proven that quality of life and quality of care are possible.

We thank the readers of our preliminary report, *A Citizens Action Guide: Nursing Home Reform*, whose enthusiastic letters, queries, and critical comments provided us with further insights and strategies for change.

We are especially grateful to Maggie Kuhn and the Gray Panther Movement, the people old and young who are working together for social justice and an end to age discrimination.

L.L.H.   E.L.G.

ix

INTRODUCTION

In America today, people are segregated and stereotyped by age, just as they are by race and sex. Gray Panthers are working across the country to wipe out agism and the frustration and despair age discrimination has created. We are a national coalition of people of various ages, focusing on the changes that are needed to make our whole society more just and human.

All sorts of changes are crucial in what has become "sickness care" rather than "health care." Consumers of various health services have rights as patients, and by affirming these rights and working together, patients can change the health care system. Furthermore, we can plan and monitor services, and take responsibility for maintaining our own physical, mental, and environmental health and well-being.

Health care has been a national priority of the Gray Panthers, and we consider long-term care to be an integral component of a comprehensive health system. The problems we have discovered in nursing homes illustrates the problems inherent in the present health system. The changes and reforms we seek in the care of nursing home residents point to overall reforms needed and mandate the organization of citizen action groups.

In our overall planning and strategy for health care reform, we are working also for alternatives to institutional care. Institutionalization is destructive both for the old who are ill and helpless as well as for young patients with more or less permanent impairments. But de-institutionalization must go hand-in-hand with institutional reform; we cannot shrug off nursing home reform for the home health bandwagon. Good nursing home care must be available for those who need it. Those who are responsible for managing institutions and the government officials who are regulating them must be held accountable to the patients and to the consumers in the community.

It is now very popular to talk about home health services. Gray Panthers nationally support home health care but not in the present fragmented form. Teams of service providers should be working on home health and the prevention of disease and dysfunction. Care should be available not upon a doctor's order or Medicare reimbursement, but as a response to consumer demands and needs.

It is our belief that alternatives to institutional care will not solve the inherent problems of long-term care. For the foreseeable future, nursing homes will be needed for some long-term care. It is our social responsibility to see that institutions meet approved standards of care and safety. Only by persistent and courageous citizen action will the present institutional scene improve.

Nursing home reformers cannot be sissies. Reform is hard and controversial. It is complicated by the fact that nursing homes reflect our society's attitude toward old age and dependency. They mirror the changes in family life and the high value we place on profits and productivity. Thus we see that the problems of the elderly in institutions are deeply rooted in the prevalent attitudes of society and its material values.

Proprietary nursing homes are big business. A great deal of federal money is poured every month into the nursing home industry through Medicare and Medicaid payments. Profit margins and "cost effectiveness," not patient needs, determine what services will be provided. The controversy over nursing homes is compounded by the fact that most nursing home residents do not know what their money should buy; what services they should expect.

Legal questions about the use of drugs as restraints, guardianships, and admission of patients who are declared incompetent often arise. The rights of families and community groups to make unannounced visits may need to be safeguarded by the courts.

American attitudes and values have often been buttressed by the negative feelings many of us have about ourselves. We hate our wrinkled bodies and fear senility. We devalue the knowledge, skills, and experience we have acquired through years of living. We step aside in order not to be a "burden."

These destructive self-images have been reinforced through the years by the findings of social science and medical research which were principally concerned with the sick and the institutionalized. These studies have only recently examined the strengths of old age, and documented the need for some basic attitudinal changes.

The advocacy of citizen groups has special rewards and benefits for all involved. It is exciting to see what positive changes occur when patients realize that they too can work for improved health care. We have seen faces light up and invigorating energy created in meetings of resident councils. When "outsiders" — the citizen action groups — and "insiders" — the resident councils — team up, there can be new life and hope.

The following pages describe tested strategy for change. We hope this book will be priority reading for members of churches, state and area agencies on aging staff, and state and federal government employees. We especially commend the guide to students in medical and nursing schools, schools of social work and gerontology, and especially the concerned families and friends of nursing home residents. Gray Panthers believe this is a new age of liberation and self-determination. Let's make the most of it!

Maggie Kuhn   National Convener   Gray Panthers

part 1: organizing

NURSING HOMES: THE ISSUES AND
NEED FOR REFORM

The long-term care required by the old and disabled should be one of the most tender and effective services a society provides. Those with potential need have increased significantly from three million in 1900 to twenty-one million people over the age of sixty-five in 1975. The very old, those over seventy-five years of age, are the fastest growing of all population groups.

Few words other than "nursing homes" are more capable of striking fear, anxiety and despair among the old. Over 1.2 million people are in nursing homes in which care ranges from excellent to negligible. Rather than live their years in peace with possibilities for self-determination and growth, too many exist in an atmosphere devoid of personal contacts and communication; too many reside in facilities which do not meet minimum standards for health, welfare, and safety. Thousands of elderly and disabled have not received adequate care and humane treatment; thousands are in facilities inappropriate to their needs and perhaps need not be there at all.

Many studies and news stories have stressed that "only five percent of the elderly are in nursing homes." That figure is misleading since it represents only the number of elderly in nursing homes on any given day. An important study by Dr. Robert Kastenbaum of Wayne State University concludes: "While one in 20 seniors is in a nursing home or related facility on any given day, one out of five seniors will spend some time in a nursing home during a lifetime."[1]

The need for long-term care includes home care, an alternative to nursing home care. A report prepared for the United

States Senate Special Committee on Aging estimates that 2.6 million people over sixty-five need in-home services. Institutionalization could have been postponed or prevented for thousands of nursing home residents if alternative services had been available. Some 2.5 million elderly are not having their needs met for home health care, supportive services, and meal services. As a consequence, their condition may deteriorate, necessitating institutionalization.

Public officials have ignored the growing public demand that sufficient money be made available to develop alternative services. Not only is there a dramatic cost savings, but home health care can service people better. Home health care may mean that thousands of elderly can remain independent in their own homes where they really want to be.

The Failure of Public Policy

Despite the expenditure of billions of tax dollars; new federal and state laws; and the pronouncements of elected officials, representatives of the health professions, and nursing home industry, a clear, constructive, and progressive policy has not yet been initiated to meet the long-term care needs of the elderly. This failure in public policy has led Senator Frank Moss, Chairman of the Subcommittee on Long-Term Care of the Senate Special Committee on Aging, to state, ". . . long-term care for older Americans stands today as the most troubled, and troublesome, component of our entire health care system."[2]

Senator Moss's grim assessment has been substantiated by a description and analysis of the full dimensions of our intolerable failure in public policy. The Senate Subcommittee on Long-Term Care has presented the facts to the American public in its series of reports, *Nursing Home Care in the United States: Failure in Public Policy.* The Introductory Report and nine supporting papers, each dealing with specific issues and providing recommendations for reform, cover fifteen years of fact-finding, 36 Senate hearings and about 3000 pages of testimony.

In preparing the extensive Moss report, Val Halamandaris, associate counsel for the subcommittee, has given us an invaluable tool for identifying the issues and initiating and supporting nursing home reform. Since it is not the purpose of this guide to describe and analyze in detail the history and current status of long-term care issues and problems, we refer the reader to the Moss report and other existing documents. The Resource section at the end of this book lists sources and available publications and summarizes the major findings of the Moss Introductory Report and each of the supporting papers.

The High Cost of Poor Care

The nursing home industry has grown rapidly in just a few decades. Since the enactment of Medicare and Medicaid, federal financial support has grown from millions to billions. In 1960 there were 9,582 facilities and 33,000 beds. By 1970 the number of facilities increased 140 percent and the number of beds increased 232 percent.[3] Total revenues for the industry in 1960 were $500 million. By 1970 they had increased 460 percent to $2.8 billion. In 1974, revenues reached an estimated $7.5 billion, a 1400 percent increase from 1960. In 1974, Medicare paid only $3.5 million of the nation's nursing home bill, but Medicaid contributed about 50 percent, a total of $3.7 billion. Thus, more than $1 out of every $2 in nursing home revenues comes from the taxpayer through public funds.[4]

There is virtually no agreement about average cost of providing nursing home care, but the average monthly charge is about $600. Since the average Social Security benefit for a retired couple is about $310 a month, most older Americans cannot afford long-term care.

Many people have been led to believe that at age sixty-five their health and nursing home care needs will be provided and paid for by Medicare. One hundred days of nursing home care is authorized under Part A of Medicare but only in very limited circumstances. Eligibility is restrictive and those who do qualify must pay $10.50 per day beginning with the twenty-first day. In 1973 only seventy thousand of the one million patients had their care paid by Medicare and only 1.67 percent of the total Medicare expenditures went for nursing home care.

The reason for this is complex, involving congressional intent at the time Medicare was enacted and an administrative shift in policy in 1969. The Medicare "extended care benefit" was intended to meet limited objectives: post-hospitalization care during convalescence. Nursing homes were allowed to participate in the reimbursement program if they met high standards and provided "skilled nursing care." These facilities were then to be known as extended care facilities (ECFs).

The ECF program boomed in numbers and costs in 1967 and 1968 — nursing home stock became one of the hottest items on the stock exchange. Medicare then provided a great assistance to the elderly in nursing homes with payments totaling $340 million.

In 1969 the rising costs resulted in a federal administrative decision to reduce payments. Benefits were cut back by requiring a patient to have "rehabilitative potential" (which excludes the terminal patient) and by narrowly defining skilled nursing care. A year later the benefit level dropped more than fifty percent to $150 million.

Since Medicare is now of little help, those in need of long-term care have looked to the welfare program Medicaid for assistance. Until 1972, Medicaid also paid only for "skilled nursing care," and the definition varied from state to state. Costs soon escalated causing critics to stress that many patients did not need skilled care. This resulted in congressional authorization of intermediate care facilities (ICFs), a less intensive level of nursing home care.

The Failure of Inspection and Enforcement

In 1972 Congress enacted Public Law 92-603, mandating a wide variety of major changes in Social Security, Medicare, and Medicaid laws. One change called for unified standards for skilled nursing facilities under Medicare and Medicaid and required HEW to develop uniform definitions for levels of care.

Although these changes were hailed as a major advance because standards were raised and there would be only one set of inspections, the consequences have been far from desirable. The standards were significantly weakened. Important standards were deleted, diluted, or nullified by exceptions. Generalizations were substituted for specifics.

The lack of specific standards makes inspection and enforcement almost impossible. And new or stronger standards are virtually meaningless as long as existing minimal regulations are not enforced. The inspection and enforcement system has generally been haphazard, fragmented, and inadequate. An entire chapter of the Moss introductory report is devoted to "Nursing Home Inspections: A National Farce."

State agencies have been reluctant to assume an enforcement and regulatory role. In many states, inspectors are not called inspectors, but field representatives, surveyors, or consultants. In describing their functions, one HEW regional director said his staff are taught to regard themselves as "guests and not as policemen." While consultant and education roles are important to bring facilities into compliance, they are not always sufficient to enforce compliance.

There is little public support, or consistently demonstrated public concern, motivating inspectors to check facilities thoroughly and to document deficiencies. For the same reason, agencies may not always enforce standards and demand that deficiencies be corrected.

Most nursing homes are given only one thorough licensure inspection a year. It is common to give advance notice. This allows a facility ample opportunity to disguise any defects for the day's inspection.

Inspectors who do report abuses and deficiences and propose appropriate plans for correction are at times disregarded or overruled by superiors. According to a *New York Times* article,[5] four former New York City inspectors testified that their critical reports on substandard homes had been suppressed by superiors who then renewed the licenses. Testimony revealed that they had been ordered to "focus on the positive" — no matter how bad conditions were. As a result, "some owners of substandard homes were sent brief congratulatory letters instead of a list of their violations, letters that were jokingly called 'love letters.' "

Due to lack of enforcement, nursing homes stay in business for an inexcusable period before deficiencies are corrected. It is uncommon for a state to adhere to definite time limits for correcting deficiencies, and only rarely is a facility closed by a state agency. In most states, the only action an agency can take against a home with uncorrected deficiencies is formal proceedings for license revocation. They are not only very costly and lengthy, but are in most instances avoided because of the standard cry, "If you close the facility, where will we put the patients?" Options are rarely available. Consequently, state officials, as well as community members, rationalize that a substandard facility is better than none at all.

Another basic problem is fragmented responsibility for nursing home activities. In most states, one government agency inspects and licenses facilities, another reimburses, a third assigns residents, and still another may be responsible for instituting legal proceedings to close a facility. Such fragmentation does not promote accountability.

A Litany of Abuses

In December 1974 the Moss subcommittee released supporting paper number 1, "The Litany of Nursing Home Abuses and an Examination of the Roots of Controversy." The report concludes that nursing home abuses, ranging from negligence leading to death and injury to profiteering and cheating the system, are widespread. In attempting to answer the question, how many nursing homes are substandard, the subcommittee determined that "it is conceivable that every nursing home in the Nation violates at least one of the many applicable standards." The subcommittee concluded that over fifty percent of the U.S. nursing homes are substandard to the extent that "they have serious and life-threatening (as opposed to technical) violations."

To support this statistic, the report cites seven sources: (1) thousands of complaint letters received by congressional committees, congressmen, and the HEW ombudsman programs; (2) fifty major newspaper exposes on nursing homes; (3) the judgments and conclusions of expert testimony; (4) independent studies, such as the Ralph Nader report; (5) surveys conducted by state and federal governments; (6) studies by independent agencies, such as the Cost of Living Council, and (7) the findings and pronouncements from the executive branch, specifically HEW and the White House.

Some of the specific problems in nursing homes, identified time and time again in newspapers, documented reports, public records, and consumer letters, include the following:

• Unsafe and unsanitary physical conditions

• Poorly trained or untrained nursing home personnel

- Low salary levels and high turnover rate for personnel
- Insufficient staff to meet patient needs
- Lack of medical care and/or medical supervision
- Lack of nursing care and/or supervision
- Inadequate food service
- Poorly controlled and uncontrolled drug practices
- No protection of residents' legal rights
- No opportunity for resident involvement in decisionmaking
- Lack of rehabilitative and preventive health care
- Lack of social and recreational services
- Physical and mental abuses
- Inappropriate placement according to level of care needed by patient
- Lack of cost accounting and cost controls

Eighty percent of the nation's nursing homes operate for profit. In contrast, eight-seven percent of all hospitals are non-profit institutions. Nursing home owners and administrators claim Medicare and Medicaid reimbursement rates are too low and cannot be the basis for profiteering. Sworn testimony before the Senate Special Subcommittee on Aging, however, refutes that claim and, in fact, includes reports that cutting expenses to the point of harming patients is not uncommon. Testimony "relates to operators who cut back on staff, spend as little as 37 cents per patient per day for food, weigh meat on a stamp scale, serve 'mock meatloaf' or breakfasts of one-half a slice of bread and coffee, and refuse to buy toothbrushes, toothpaste, toilet paper or other necessities."[6]

The public has a right to be critical of the industry's cries for more money. Full-scale auditing of all nursing homes receiving tax money could give the public a clear view of the financial picture. During the period from 1966 to 1975, twenty states did not conduct a single audit of Medicaid-eligible long-term care facilities. Where audits did take place, it was usually because of a major nursing home scandal uncovered by the news media.

In October 1974, the *New York Times* began a series of articles by John Hess on nursing home problems. Grounded on extensive research, these articles soon attracted attention to the financial manipulations to defraud the government and the resulting poor care.

In state after state, investigations and audits have exposed nursing homes which have abused federal and state reimbursement programs, and therefore, the residents and general public. Cheating and excess profits at the expense of residents and the taxpayers must cease. Nursing homes must be held accountable for the money they receive as well as the type of care they provide.

As the Moss report indicates, the precise number of substandard facilities is not the issue. If there were only "isolated instances" of substandard facilities among the nation's twenty-three thousand homes, there would still be a need for an active reform program. In response to any reports of nursing home abuse, the industry generally counterattacks with standard responses: the critic who has exposed the abuse is "untrained and inexperienced" or one who "overreacts"; if a patient or resident makes the complaint, the patient is "old and confused"; and if family members initiate the complaint, they are labeled "guilty children." *Always* the alleged abuses are labeled "isolated instances." The Moss report recommends that the "time for denials and mutual recriminations is long past. It is time for operators and consumer advocates to work together in the spirit of trust and good will if there is to be an improvement in the quality of life for the Nation's 1 million nursing home patients."

"Nursing Homes" Without Nurses

Nursing home work and providing health services to the elderly infirm has little attraction for qualified workers. A very high turnover rate and shortage of qualified personnel results in a reliance on untrained personnel for patient care. It is a hoax to call these institutions "nursing homes" when in most instances there are no nursing services. Of the 722,200 nursing home personnel, only seven percent are registered nurses, and eight percent are licensed practical nurses. And they are usually involved with administration rather than providing or directly supervising patient care.

Nurse aides and orderlies perform about eighty to ninety percent of the patient care in nursing homes. Very few are adequately trained. In fact, many are literally hired right off the street. The service aides provide is probably the most difficult and the most demanding. Most are grossly overworked and underpaid. To make it worse, they are also the least respected health care workers and receive no public recognition, support or rewards for their services.

Another major problem is the absence of physicians. The medical profession has failed to take responsibility for nursing home patients. Providing services in a nursing home is simply not viewed as part of the medical continuum. Part of this failure can be attributed to the negative image of caring for the old and chronically ill, as well as a lack of adequate training in geriatrics and gerontology in medical schools.

Residents Without Rights

As citizens we have rights enabling us to live fully and freely. Our dignity as human beings relates directly to the extent that we can exercise these rights. Although nursing home residents are entitled to the full spectrum of rights enjoyed by other citizens, exercising them is often a difficult process. The fact that specific provisions for patient rights had to be included in new federal regulations indicates the extent to which many nursing home residents have been dehumanized, victimized and abused.

Nursing home residents want to come and go as freely as their physical condition permits, have visitors, obtain information about their care, have space for privacy and possessions, and become actively involved in decisions regarding the policies and services affecting their daily lives. These desires can be in direct conflict with the nursing home's interest in efficient administration — for maximum profit on their investment.

A nursing home's profit will usually be higher when it (1) employs a minimum number of staff; (2) spends a minimal amount on patient activities, services, and food; and (3) allocates minimal space per person and limited space for activities and support services. When staff, space, and time are limited, the result is strict maintenance of order, strict adherence to set daily routines.

Other factors influence the residents' ability or desire to

exercise their rights. They are often alone, isolated from the community-at-large and even from other residents. Estimates vary, but because most patients are in their seventies and eighties, about fifty percent have no active relationship with a close relative. Most nursing home residents do not have visitors.

Most residents have physical or health problems which affect their energy to act. Studies show that patients generally have about four chronic or crippling disabilities. Less than half can walk and many take large quantities of drugs. Many would have no other place to live so they dare not challenge the pattern of behavior expected of them and directed towards them.

Investigations and recognition of infringement and wholesale denial of individual rights set the stage in the early 1970s for federal and state reform efforts. Interest heightened after the American Hospital Association adopted a patients' bill of rights in 1972. The HEW work on resident rights was spearheaded by Allan Forman, director of the federal Nursing Home Ombudsman Demonstration Program. With the additional help of Halamandaris of the Moss subcommittee staff, and Marilyn Schiff, director of the Nursing Home Ombudsman Program of the National Council of Senior Citizens, regulations for patient rights were promulgated in 1974 and 1975.

Enforcing patients' rights regulations for skilled and intermediate care facilities will be difficult. A major limitation: the regulations require that facilities create the necessary procedures to assure enforcement. This is unrealistic because most nursing home operators saw no need for such regulations in the first place.

The attitude of individual administrators and nursing home staff has been and will remain a barrier to effective implementation of rights regulations — an attitude exemplified by:

• Denial that resident rights are being violated;

• Statement that residents are ill, therefore not concerned about asserting their rights;

• Warnings that residents are confused and senile and would not understand even if advised of their rights;

• Claims that residents need protection or they would not be in a nursing home;

• Opinions that residents are not alert and knowledgeable enough to be involved in decisionmaking regarding facility policies and services.

We cannot expect that administrators and staff who raise such arguments will voluntarily do more than hand out mimeographed copies of regulations and draw up plans and procedures which never go beyond paper compliance. Administrators and staff — as well as the inspectors and the general public — need training about resident rights. Education must often begin with basic consciousness-raising about the individual freedoms of citizens in institutions.

Federal Efforts at Reform

In the summer of 1971, substandard nursing homes were the central topic of a major presidential address on problems of the aged. The president announced an eight-point nursing home reform program including training of state nursing home inspectors; authorizing one hundred percent federal reimbursement for the costs of state inspections; expanding the federal enforcement program with new staff; cutting off federal funds to facilities not meeting standards; training of nursing home personnel; creation of demonstration ombudsman programs; a comprehensive study of long-term care facilities; and the centralization of enforcement activities within one HEW office.

The Moss introductory report provides a point-by-point critical analysis of the reform program and the resulting federal action. Two points merit special attention in this overview. Centralizing responsibility for enforcement activities resulted in the creation of the Office of Nursing Home Affairs (ONHA) in HEW's Public Health Service. The two divisions created in ONHA are the Division of Standards Enforcement Coordination and the Division of Policy Development. ONHA works directly with the Offices of Long-Term Care Standards Enforcement in all of the HEW regional offices to advise and administer activities relating to certification of skilled nursing facilities. The Division of Policy Development interprets and develops policies relating to both institutional and noninstitutional long-term care.

In 1974 ONHA announced the Long-Term Care Facility Improvement Campaign (LTCFIC), a multi-faceted effort directed towards upgrading the quality of care and increasing compliance to federal standards. A "statistically valid" survey of 295 nursing homes was conducted to provide baseline data on the quality of care to identify needs, develop programs to meet those needs, and to measure the success of federal reform initiatives.

The findings, published in an introductory report, July 1975, cite widespread deficiencies in U.S. nursing homes including overdrugging, inadequate medical attention, inadequate diets, poor rehabilitation programs and fire safety violations. The survey also documented "that paper compliance alone provides insufficient evidence to show that quality care is being provided."

ONHA's major thrust to improve and better evaluate patient care is a review of the survey/certification process. This will be accomplished through PACE, Patient Assessment Care Evaluation, which involves the training of state inspectors and nursing home providers to use a patient assessment approach as an evaluation and management tool. Theorized as a better way to regulate nursing homes, PACE will be studied, developed, tested, and implemented over the next five years.

The Long-Term Care Facility Improvement Campaign will ultimately address other issues including the development of a computerized information system and a monthly cost of care index; and a nationwide uniform inspection and rating system program.

HEW's state nursing home consumer complaint investigative units were initiated in 1972 with the funding of nursing home ombudsman demonstration projects in seven states: Idaho, Pennsylvania, South Carolina, Wisconsin, Michigan, Massachusetts, and Oregon. The announced purpose was to (1) resolve residents' complaints; (2) document significant problems in the nursing home field; and (3) test the effectiveness of volunteers in resolving problems of nursing home residents.

In 1973, administrative responsibility for these projects was transferred within HEW from ONHA to the Administration on Aging (AoA).

In 1975 Senator Moss proposed legislation requiring all states to establish ombudsman programs to investigate nursing home complaints and represent consumer interests. This proposal and the ombudsman program experience under AoA influenced Arthur Flemming, United States Commissioner on Aging, to initiate the development of ombudsman projects in every state.

In May 1975 state agencies on aging were invited to submit proposals to promote effective statewide ombudsman activities. Forty-seven states, Puerto Rico, and the District of Columbia applied for and received the Title III (Older Americans Act) funding for an initial one-year period.

It was clear that the ombudsman's role was to be service-oriented — to receive, investigate, and resolve nursing home complaints. When AoA organized the first training event for ombudsmen in October 1975, however, the role had been changed considerably. The ombudsman was now to be called "ombudsman development specialist," responsible for providing overall leadership in planning and service areas and in promoting nursing home ombudsman activities. This person was not to provide direct services to patients or handle complaints. The change came as a major surprise to many state agencies which had already publicly announced the creation of a statewide program to help resolve citizen complaints. Needless to say, consumer advocate groups were also disturbed with the change.

The new goal is to develop a voluntary ombudsman process at the local community level which will respond to complaints. The ombudsman development specialist is to approach every area agency on aging to explain the goals of the program and encourage agencies to provide leadership and initiate a voluntary ombudsman program. The area agencies would organize a "panel of community volunteers" to receive and act on complaints. These agencies would also organize relatives of patients and publicize nursing home issues in a systematic manner to the public and government. The agencies were advised that the panel of volunteers should not include nursing home providers or representatives of regulatory bodies with jurisdiction over nursing homes.

The AoA ombudsman development specialist program is historical because it recognizes the magnitude and social significance of the problems and that they must be tackled on a state-by-state, community-by-community basis. It also identified the inherent problems and conflict of interest involved in allowing traditional government regulatory agencies and the nursing home industry to take the lead in any program development.

There is, however, considerable reason to question the real impact this program can have. The insights gained in an evaluation of the first seven HEW demonstration ombudsman projects were not applied in developing the AoA ombudsman program. These issues include the following:

(1) Volunteers are valuable, but they need close supervision

and training requiring considerable staff time.

(2) After more than three years of operation demonstration ombudsman staff are still developing the necessary expertise to deal with all the complex issues and many diverse organizations and agencies in the delivery system. A full-time, knowledgeable staff is required to handle the complexities of a complaint and monitoring system as well as provide education and information to the public.

(3) Problems and complaints need to be resolved quickly. The ombudsman should not have to go through several offices to resolve complaints, and the public should not have to wait for or rely on volunteers to assist them.

(4) To be fully effective, ombudsman staff need statutory authority to make changes. They need to be able to subpoena records and make full investigations without having to rely on voluntary cooperation.

(5) Rather than alerting the public to critical problems, ombudsman staff often must remain silent and "neutral" because they cannot afford to anger or embarrass the agencies and industry.

(6) The ombudsmen have demonstrated that they cannot stick to the classic model of ombudsmen who remain impartial. To effect change and improve the system, ombudsmen have had to act as advocates.

(7) The projects have vividly demonstrated that it takes a substantial budget to maintain a qualified staff and an effective program.

A harsh reality is that the AoA funding for the nationwide ombudsman program will not begin to cover the costs of an effective reform program. Thirty-eight states received only $18,000 each. Grants for the other nine states ranged from $21,000 to $58,000. In comparison, the final year of funding for the seven demonstration projects totaled $1,862,276, and that was considered inadequate. Clearly the amounts doled out to the states was only a token, and the funding for the second year is expected to remain the same. In 1975 $105 million was appropriated for all Title III projects. Perhaps if only $6 million to $7 million had been set aside for nursing home programs, strong state reform programs might have been developed.

ORGANIZING A CITIZENS' ACTION
GROUP

As a society, we have decided to entrust the care of thousands of Americans to nursing homes. The nursing home industry has failed that trust. Its special interests are represented
and protected by skilled attorneys, highly paid lobbyists, and
public relations firms. Public pressure must begin to counter-
act powerful industry pressure. A *National Journal* article
(July 4, 1970) states that the nursing home lobby is "effective
particularly because it has little opposition from consumers."

As a society, we have decided to entrust to our government
the health, welfare, and safety of older people in nursing
homes. The government too has failed that trust. Decisions
affecting long-term care are most often made by a few people
in high places, removed from and out of touch with those affected by their decisions. Government regulatory agencies are
too often understaffed, underfinanced, and carry out their
responsibilities in a fragmented, haphazard manner. In support
of citizen advocacy, the Post-White House Conference on
Aging recognized that continual monitoring by other than governmental agencies is necessary to insure public responsiveness.

As a society, we have decided to entrust to health professionals, physicians, nurses, social workers, and others the health
and welfare of the aged and disabled in nursing homes. They
too have failed. The medical profession has not taken medical
responsibility and has shunned patients in nursing homes.
Nurses and social workers have generally maintained a conspir-
acy of silence by not reporting or acting on abuses and deficiencies they witness. Educational institutions, for the most
part, continue to perpetuate the negative image of old people

and the negative image of caring for old people by failing to recognize and provide curricula in geriatrics and gerontology.

There are forces at work in our society to promote the health and welfare of nursing home residents. Individuals, groups, and organizations which are a part of that movement should be recognized and commended. As responsible citizens, we can no longer avoid our own responsibility to solve the problems inherent in the long-term care system.

Citizen involvement and community action at the local, state, and national level are necessary and vital factors for fundamental reform. Yet, if public concern regarding long-term care is to be effective, it will have to be developed and focused in a careful, systematic way. Since the forces protecting the present system are strong, community groups need to be even stronger. We can make real changes only if people organize and make a commitment to work together. Remember, it may not be the numbers involved, but rather the degree of commitment, talent, and sustained effort that counts in making changes.

The real impetus for organizing nursing home reform will come from individuals and community groups. Identifying or organizing an action group may be time consuming, but it is an important first step in problem solving. As a group, you will not only be able to divide the work more efficiently and effectively, but you will probably be more effective as a source of power and pressure to correct nursing home problems. If for example, one person visits a state licensure agency and says: "I've found this deficiency and I think it should be corrected," it is doubtful that that person could exert much influence. If (s)he went to the agency and said: "I am a member of a group of thirty citizens and we have decided that this deficiency must be corrected," (s)he would be noticed.

Individual citizen action for nursing home reform is not uncommon. In fact, many organized groups described in Part Three were stimulated by and progressed because of the actions of one, two, or three committed individuals. The individuals saw the need to find support for their work and to organize an action group. Most organizers were not able to take time to think through a step-by-step process of organizing, but in reviewing their activities it became clear that they did take certain actions and observed certain organizing strategies, which can be shared with others.

A lesson learned from existing citizen action groups is that anyone and everyone has the potential for being an organizer. Organizing a citizen action group will require a substantial commitment of time, energy, and in most instances, money. If you choose to organize a group, there are some basic considerations you can readily learn and incorporate into your organizational plan. There is a wealth of resource materials available on the techniques of organizing and some are listed in the Resources section. The following is a general overview of basic organizing principles.

Getting Started

If you have seemed alone in your concern about nursing home conditions, probably the first thing you'll want to do is to get a few sympathetic and understanding friends together to talk about the problems. This could be a time for sharing experiences and attitudes each has about nursing homes and growing old.

If there are two or more of you, concerned, angry, ready to begin some action, you should decide on an overall goal. You must know why you are organizing; this general goal will determine the kind of organization and citizen action group necessary to achieve it. For example, if your overall goal is to determine ownership patterns of facilities in your community, you might only need two or three persons to search records in the county courthouse for a couple of weeks. If your goal is to show strong support for a particular legislative bill, you might want to organize one hundred people for a bus caravan to the state capital to testify at a hearing.

Inquire whether an existing group is working on the issue. Call such organizations as the Council of Churches, health and welfare council, the area agency on aging, Catholic Charities. If an activity is underway you may want to consider joining forces. Or, you might consider asking an organization to which you already belong to support your efforts. If the organization is large and involved with many issues you can suggest forming a special task force on nursing homes.

The potential membership or constituency for a new action group is almost endless. The central question is "Whose problem is it and who is being most affected by it?" People are impelled to organize and act on an issue not by some philosophical theory or abstract vision alone, but because they have recognized that conditions have become intolerable. We will all grow old some day — a nursing home can be in anyone's future. On the practical side, all taxpayers are affected by the issue since about one out of every two dollars in nursing home revenue comes from some form of public payment.

It is crucial that older citizens be involved and begin to take initiative in confronting the nursing home industry and the government to demand nursing home reform. The involvement of older people can be a great asset to any action group. They have the time, wisdom, experience, demands of their own, a taste of class oppression, and many need active community involvement to overcome the despair, depression, and isolation society has conditioned them to accept as part of their old age.

Your group should include knowledgeable people with first-hand experiences with nursing homes. They might be relatives and friends of nursing home residents and of course, residents themselves. One obstacle you might meet in attempting to organize relatives, friends, and residents is fear of reprisal, a legitimate fear that has undoubtedly prevented many complaints from being aired. But if one is not standing alone, but is part of a strong group, the fear of threats of physical or mental reprisals is lessened. Residents are more apt to effectively assert and establish their rights if they have a strong source of outside support.

People of all age groups should contribute to your efforts. Young people can certainly contribute idealism, vision, and physical energy. And an increasing number of younger people with chronic and disabling conditions are in need of nursing home care. Also, an increasing number of retarded children and young adults are housed in nursing homes. Enlist their parents, or a community association representing the retarded and the physically disabled, in your efforts.

To recruit active membership you might want to call a public meeting to sensitize people to the problems and to outline your goals for action. Use a telephone chain: have each person call five friends to attend the meeting. Send letters or make personal appearances before local civic groups, women's church groups or senior citizen and nutrition centers. Put an ad in the local paper. Distribute and post fliers announcing the meeting and the group's formation, and don't forget to distribute them to nursing homes. If the nursing home administrator does not allow you to post your announcement, pass the fliers out to residents and their visitors.

People attending your first meeting will be coming from different walks of life — with different lifestyles, attitudes, skills, and expertise — and each will have his/her reason for attending. It is important to "start where people are at." You will need to care about these people, be concerned about their needs and ideas, tolerant of personal styles and choices. Some might be ready to march on the state capital protesting nursing home conditions to the governor while others might want to arrange a library service at the local facility. See that each member's skill, expertise, or degree of involvement is used to the maximum. Channel responses, don't let enthusiastic volunteers lose their steam. Action can grow out of felt needs, and anger and outrage are powerful stimulants. Sign them up for special projects or give them specific assignments. For those that may only want to initiate a "friendly visitor" program and don't really see themselves yet as advocates, remember that service can lead to advocacy.

When presenting your organization to new and prospective members, be truthful and accurate concerning your program and your initial goals. Once recruited, provide each individual with a thorough orientation and then set each of them to work immediately. The absence of a clear purpose will halt progress. It is essential that goals be well defined from the start. Equally important is that each member have a sense of identity and purpose within the group and a reason for returning to another meeting. Give specific assignments or tasks to each member. It may be as simple as reading an article or reviewing classified ads in the yellow pages for nursing homes and reporting the findings. Often apathy and hopelessness about the real possibility for changing conditions poses a serious problem in getting started. Becoming organized and beginning work fights this apathy. Capitalize on this accomplishment; congratulate yourselves on every new member. Organizing is the first step and once you have made that step, you are well on your way.

Three key roles which should be identified and assigned early in developing the group are organizer, leader, and administrator. (All three roles may be performed by one person until the work load demands that they be divided.) The organizer is the facilitator, the one who ensures that leadership is developed and gives the group direction. The leader is the skilled, competent, and confident individual who can serve as an effective spokesperson. The administrator serves in a technical role; making arrangements for a meeting place, arranging for coffee and plenty of chairs, making certain that phone bills are paid, etc. Once you begin to know the members of your new group, you can easily identify persons for these roles. In fact, these individuals might automatically emerge and begin functioning on their own.

Although membership is an important organization resource, identify other resources which might be needed to reach your goals. You might begin operations out of your own home where you will need to maintain a card file on all your contacts and members. You'll want names, addresses, phone numbers, specific areas of interest or expertise, and information on how often members will be available. The telephone is the most important channel for communication; make sure your members have your number. You might prefer to rent a post office box for correspondence. Check with your church or community center for the use of office equipment such as a typewriter and mimeograph machine. Churches, schools, and community centers are good places to hold meetings, if convenient to public transportation. As your organization grows, you may find it necessary to have an office. Again, investigate the possibility of churches, schools, or community centers donating office space.

Getting Funds

The question of finances will probably be raised early in your organizing efforts. An operating and program budget is important but not imperative for action. Voluntary citizen action groups have accomplished great things without much money. Don't let money be the only concern of your group. Many groups become ineffective and eventually dissolve because they concentrate all their energies on fundraising.

Although fundraising can be a constant problem, it need not be limited to any particular technique nor require an expert for success. A fundraising committee might be formed with those individuals who have done fundraising in the past as members. You can meet initial organizational needs by passing the hat. Some groups have a minimal annual dues program, although, as your program ideas and activities grow, this may not be an adequate nor consistent source of income.

One source of private financing, usually available only to voluntary nonprofit groups, is foundation grants. Two sources of foundation names and addresses are: (1) *Foundation News*, a monthly magazine listing many grants by subject category and agency names and (2) *The Foundation Directory* (Columbia University Press), which also lists grants given on an annual basis. The directory is more complete but less current than *Foundation News*. These publications can be found in most public or university libraries.

Another source of financial support might be the local business community. The chamber of commerce can provide a list of most small and large businesses and industry in your area. Designate a member to contact these firms, preferably in person, for contributions.

Churches and synagogues can be a major source of financial support. Many of the major churches, such as the Presbyterians, Lutherans, Episcopalians, and Unitarian-Universalists, have special issue-related programs and fund special organizations and institutions.

Government funding — federal, state, county, or city — is another possible source of revenue. Recently government funds have been used to assist groups in building membership and in self-education for legislative and social change activities. This source may have "strings attached." Approach it with caution. Find out exactly what you have to give up to obtain funds. One group described in Part Three, Citizens for Better Care in Detroit, has been successful in obtaining government funds while maintaining an active advocacy role. With funding from the regional HEW Office of Long-Term Care Standards Enforcement, the Denver Gray Panthers were able to conduct two training workshops on consumer advocacy and nursing homes.

Explore the idea of hiring a student through the local college, professional school placement office, or field education office. A student can contract to work as an intern and be paid by a federal work-study grant. A group will have to provide a small amount of seed money, usually about one-quarter of the student's salary. Citizens for the Improvement of Nursing

Homes, Seattle, has obtained two full-time student staff persons with a very small investment.

Educational institutions usually have a commitment to human service and programs of social change and are looking for groups to provide actual field experiences for students. Many undergraduate and graduate departments, especially social work and urban studies, offer course and field placement credit for students who work with community groups. In most instances there is no financial requirement, but a group will be responsible for supervising and evaluating the work of a student. Colleges usually require that the supervisory role be filled by a professional person; someone with a degree in social work or some other human service field. Sometimes other community agencies, such as an area agency on aging, can provide supervision and arrange to have one of these students assigned to an action group.

Citizens for Better Care has been successful in activating yet another source for staff support through VISTA (Volunteers in Service to America) of the ACTION program. ACTION is a federal program which initiates and coordinates volunteer programs. Other ACTION programs include: Foster Grandparents, Retired Senior Volunteer Program (RSVP), and Service Corps of Retired Executives (SCORE). Information on any of these programs can be obtained through the ACTION regional office, usually listed in the telephone book under "U.S. Government."

The Pros and Cons of Incorporating

Some action groups have legally incorporated to obtain non-profit, tax-exempt status. There are certain advantages to incorporating. A formalized and sometimes permanent structure is set in place and donors can get tax deductions for contributions to incorporated groups.

Many groups never feel the need to incorporate and yet are successful in obtaining money for operating expenses and special projects. There are disadvantages to incorporation. It may limit political activity. It can be both costly and complicated, although some groups are able to get CPA and legal services from professional volunteers or community agencies.

The primary document of incorporation is the charter; the legal authorization for the organization which states its purpose. As a nonprofit group, you would probably file an application as a charitable, religious, or educational organization.

Depending on your activities and how you intend to function in the future, the organization can seek tax-exempt status under 26 United States Code 501(c) 3 or under 26 United States Code 501(c) 4:

- 501(c) 3 status is granted to corporations organized and operated exclusively for "religious, charitable, scientific, testing for public safety, literacy or educational purposes . . . "
- 501(c) 4 status is accorded to corporations "not organized for profit but operated exclusively for the promotion of social welfare."

Groups incorporated under either category cannot campaign on behalf of a candidate for public office.

The 501(c) 3 status is the more difficult to get. Its primary advantage: it permits donors to deduct contributions from their taxable income. Under this category a corporation can institute public education and research any issue. But, it can only get involved in *limited* litigation and it *cannot* devote any substantial time and activities to lobbying. Furthermore, it cannot devote any substantial part of its activities to organizing efforts which *would result* in lobbying.

A corporation with 501(c) 4 status cannot confer a tax benefit for donations, so finding sources of funding becomes more difficult, but *other advantages are clear*. In addition to being able to institute public education efforts and to research any issue, the corporation with this tax status *can do* the following: it can litigate in *almost* every area, it can lobby freely, and it can conduct citizen organizing drives which may result in lobbying.

To circumvent the constraints of either status, some groups, such as Citizens for Better Care, have established two separate corporations. One corporation applies for 501(c) 3 status to attract foundation support and carry out education and research activities, while the other would seek 501(c) 4 status for lobbying and organizing purposes. The secretary of state's office, usually located in the state capital, can furnish information about forming and operating a nonprofit corporation.

3

EDUCATION AND RESEARCH: TOOLS
FOR ACTION

Educating your membership, as well as the general public, is an important part in the process of seeking change. The best decisions are usually made after careful research and documentation of facts and an understanding of the strengths and weaknesses of forces blocking reform. Once your group feels it is strong enough — knowledgeable and well armed with facts — it can then seek ways to demonstrate its demands and initiate reform activities.

A group should not be afraid to begin investigation and research activities which might be unfamiliar. We have been socialized to believe that only a select few have the expertise to engage in serious research and that it requires a strict, academic orientation. Research simply involves the gathering of information, working with this information until a pattern emerges, and then moving into action. The group must realize that some information is essential, but there may be a problem of some group members' wanting to spend too much time and energy gathering facts. Remember, research and investigation are tools for reaching your goals.

The kinds of research and investigation you need to conduct will depend on your goals and objectives. If you decide to initiate legislation to improve the inspection system, you might not need to do power structure research, but you will need to know how to study the licensing agency, how to get access to inspection reports, and how to personally inspect nursing homes.

The greatest potential barriers to obtaining information may be government bureaucracy and the closed doors of the local nursing homes. The public has a right to know and the following two sections are designed to help your action group learn what those basic rights are.

The remaining pages describe the "why" and the "hows" of the more common education, research, and investigative programs citizens groups have become involved in. We hope these guidelines will assist people in beginning to develop their own research and investigative skills.

Freedom of Information

The federal government is a vast storehouse of untapped information. The public has a right to know if and how government agencies are carrying out their responsibilities. The Freedom of Information Act, passed in 1966, and amended in 1974, provides for public access to federal government information. The act gives the right of access, either to view or to photocopy, any record, files, administrative staff manual, or any other document in the possession of any *federal* agency or department. There are some exceptions, of course, but it is the responsibility of the government agency, not the person making the request, to prove that the request is specifically exempted. Government employees face possible sanctions if they arbitrarily withhold information. While the federal act does not apply to state or city governments, many states have their own freedom of information acts. Check with the office of your state's attorney general to determine if your state has a law similar to the federal act.

Each federal agency or department has regulations (found in the *Code of Federal Regulations*) that describe the procedure for requesting information from that particular agency. You can get further advice by calling the agency's office of public information.

The first step is to determine what information you want. The law states that your request must "reasonably describe" the records or documents you want. While you will not need to specify the information by exact name, title or number, you do want to give enough descriptive information to get what you want. This will make it difficult for the government to refuse your request on the claim that it is too vague. If the specific title of a report, document, or inspection record is

known, then make the request specific. It is also a good idea
to request "any other documents or information relating to
the subject." The agency will only provide what you specifically ask for, even though other valuable information may be
available.

If you have a general idea of what you want, but need further identifying information to obtain it, check the indices at
that particular agency. HEW, for example, must provide for
public inspection and copying a current index which provides
the identifying information for all disclosable matter which
was issued, adopted, or promulgated after July 4, 1967.

Your request for information must be in writing and addressed to the head of the agency or department. You should
state that the request is being made "pursuant to the Freedom
of Information Act (5 U.S.C. Sec. 552)." You are not required
to say why you want the information. The request should also
state that if you receive no response within ten working days,
you will assume that the request has been denied and will take
further action to get the information. The agency is required
by law to respond within ten working days of receipt of the
request, so when you include such a statement, you're telling
the official that you know your rights under the law.

If you receive notification that your request has been
denied, you have the right to appeal. A letter should be sent to
the head of the agency, stating what information you have
requested, that your request was denied, and that an appeal is
now being made with the agency. The agency has twenty working days to respond to your appeal. If the appeal is denied,
you may pursue legal action in the United States District
Court.

The Freedom of Information Act permits agencies to charge
for direct costs of searching for information and for copying
documents. The fee schedules for HEW are published in the
Federal Register. The fee for search of records is $3.00 per
hour; no charges, however, will be made for the first thirty
minutes of the search. The charge for copying of records is ten
cents per page. The forwarding of materials, including postage,
insurance, and any special fees will be charged on an actual
cost basis. To save money, ask to see the documents in person
rather than having copies mailed to you. If you do ask for
copies, state that you will pay costs up to a certain amount.
This might prevent an unexpectedly large bill. It is possible to

request that the agency waive or reduce the fees if you are indigent or believe that disclosure of the information will primarily benefit the general public.

Access to Nursing Homes

There are two basic arguements that support efforts for free access to nursing homes. The first is based on the First Amendment of the Constitution and the second is the recent Medicare and Medicaid patients' rights regulations. In Michigan and Pennsylvania lawsuits were brought by consumer representatives groups asserting a constitutional right to nursing home access. Although neither case resulted in a court decision, both were settled on terms recognizing the plaintiffs' access rights.

In the Pennsylvania case, *Health Law Project v. Sarah Allen Nursing Home*, the plaintiffs, in a class action suit, sought an order assuring them access, and raised the following arguments. Because nursing homes serve a public function, they should be considered a quasi-public place. By denying community-service and public-interest groups access, residents are isolated from those gathering and providing information to protect their interests.

Another argument was based on the 1968 Civil Rights Act. The isolation of nursing home residents may prohibit their knowledge of rights and benefits under the Social Security or public assistance acts. The Civil Rights Act prohibits parties, which could mean nursing home personnel and owners, from interfering with the rights to participate in and enjoy "any benefit, service, privilege, program . . . provided or administered by the United States."

In October 1974 and March 1975, the Social Security Administration published patients' rights regulations for skilled nursing facilities and intermediate care facilities participating in the Medicare and Medicaid reimbursement programs. Several provisions are aimed directly at opening communications between residents and the outside world. The wording for both the SNF and ICF regulations are the same, but the section numbers are different, and are as follows:

SNF §405.1121(k)(5) and ICF §249.12(A)(5)
[The resident] Is encouraged and assisted throughout his period of stay,

to exercise his rights as a patient and as a citizen, and to this end may voice grievances and recommend changes in policies and services to facility staff and/or *outside representatives of his choice*, free from restraint, interference, coercion, discrimination or reprisal.

SNF §405.1121(k)(11) and ICF §249.12(A)(12)
May associate and communicate privately with persons of his own choice, and may send and receive his mail unopened, unless medically contraindicated (as documented by his physician in his medical record):

SNF §405.1121(k)(12) and ICF §249.12(A)(13)
May associate with, and participate in activities of social, religious, and community groups of his discretion, unless medically contraindicated (as documented by his physician in his medical record.)

There can be wide variation in interpreting these regulations. For example, it is possible for those wanting to keep groups out of the facility to arrange for a cooperative doctor to "medically contraindicate" visits, or, an administrator may tell visitors that a resident may *only* see persons "of his choice," meaning persons he has specifically asked in advance to see.

Reading and Library Research

Educating yourself and your group members to the nursing home issue can begin with reading this book, but more extensive reading will probably be necessary. The best overview of the long-term care system can be obtained by reviewing the books and reports listed below. Other important resource materials are listed in the Resources section.

Although written in 1971, the report of Ralph Nader's volunteer nursing home task force, *Old Age: The Last Segregation*, offers a good overview of nursing home problems and the activities of state and federal government. It also has a chapter on recommendations which are still relevant and need to be implemented. Mary Adelaide Mendelson's book, *Tender Loving Greed*, (1974) is a result of her ten-year study of the nursing home industry. Mendelson exposes the inner workings of the industry that talks "Tender Loving Care and Happiness Benefits" while it mistreats the old and robs us of our tax money. Government studies and journalistic exposés have reported for years the callous treatment given to patients in nursing homes. But until G. Janet Tulloch wrote *A Home Is*

Not a Home: Life Within a Nursing Home (1975), there was
no account by an actual nursing home resident which told
what it meant to be alone, old, and institutionalized. The
author emphasizes the residents' struggle for personal dignity
and individuality, showing that staff neglect and victimization
are often caused by indifference and insensitivity rather than
intentional cruelty.

Every individual or group concerned with the nursing home
issue should obtain the series of reports *Nursing Home Care in
the United States: Failure in Public Policy*, issued by the Subcommittee on Long-Term Care of the Senate Special Committee on Aging. The report covers a fifteen-year time span, 36
hearings and about 3000 pages of testimony. The introductory
report was released in November 1974. The other nine reports
discuss specific issues and offer recommendations for corrective action.

You can do research in the public library, but a college or
university library will probably be more valuable, especially if
the school offers degrees in any of the health professions. To
avoid possible duplication of research, be sure to check the
card catalogue for research papers, theses, or dissertations written on nursing homes. For example, when doing library research at the local college, members of the Davenport, Iowa,
Citizens Monitoring Team found three research studies done
by nursing students.

You should also review various professional, health, and
industry journals and publications. While reading the journals
for health professionals or nursing home administrators, look
for any possible handles that could be used to influence or
change them. What do their editorials say? How are they reacting to recent events, legislation, and new regulations? Note the
type of advertisements. For example, how many ads are promoting tranquilizers for nursing home residents? Look for articles that may be used as ammunition, but also look for pieces
that may favor your concern or describe innovation or excel-
lence. You might find a new program developed by nursing
home staff which is beneficial to residents. You could later ask
local nursing homes to implement the same type of program.

Review the monthly newsletters of the state nursing home
association. If the school, hospital, or public libraries do not
have current and back issues, try to get copies directly from
the association or from a friendly nursing home administrator.

Association members are usually kept well informed and a review of the last year's newsletters will be of great value to your group. What types of issues are operators and leaders addressing? How are they reacting to these issues? What are their organizational strategies? Who are their "friends" — are any legislators always attending special banquets as guests?

Visit Homes Informally

Once you have read background materials and become familiar with some of the problems in the long-term care system, you will need to become aware of the nursing home situation in your own community. Obviously if some members of the group have not had direct experience visiting a nursing home, this is a must. Initial visits should be on an informal basis, with the goal of acquainting people to the sights, sounds, and smells of the place called a "nursing home."

Each nursing home will vary in physical structure and the quality and quantity of services and programs. They will also vary in the number and extent of deficiencies. In each community there is usually some general unwritten knowledge of which nursing homes are "good" and which are viewed as "terrible." The new citizen action group should not create a trap for itself by making negative or positive judgments and evaluations based primarily on hearsay without first visiting the facilities. The group should either visit all the homes or a random sample of both the "good" and the "terrible" as well as those that fall somewhere in between. Although it is definitely important to identify those "terrible" homes, it is equally important to identify those facilities offering safe, high quality care, the very best in the community. Recognition and support should be given to those homes and staff who are truly concerned about the quality of life of their residents and are providing excellent programs. Identification of both the good and the bad will give the group and the general public, as well as the regulatory agencies and the industry, a basis for comparison. The better homes can be suggested as models for others to follow.

There is no one sure way to get into a nursing home to make an evaluation. One administrator might permit spontaneous visits, another might require prior appointments, still another might not let you in the door if he knows what you are doing. On the other hand, the same administrator who didn't respond to one member of your group might be persuaded by another.

If any members of your group have a friend or a relative in a nursing home, it would be best to visit this person and ask the resident to give you a tour of the facility. If there is no inside contact, one approach may be to simply go to a home and tell the person greeting you at the door that you would just like to come in, look around, and perhaps visit with a few residents who may be sitting in the lounge. You may not even need to talk with the administrator. In fact, during the first informal visit it may be best if you do not talk with the administrator. Gaining access to a nursing home for an informal visit need not be too difficult since, after all, they are considered community health facilities. Don't be discouraged if you are refused, just try another home. Be sure to note in your files which homes refused to cooperate, recording the reasons given.

Probably the best time to visit a nursing home is in the afternoon or very early evening. Mornings are usually very busy with personal care activities. Two people on a visiting team can be most effective. A larger group might frighten the personnel into thinking they were being invaded and admission might be refused.

While visiting informally, you need to be keenly attuned to the things around you. Look, smell, touch, and listen. Ask yourself these questions: How is the place run? Is there a responsible individual in charge? What is the attitude of staff toward residents? Do staff interact with residents? Are residents treated with respect and dignity or are they treated like children? Is the atmosphere rehabilitative and supportive, or custodial? Do patients interact with one another? Do residents look well cared for? Do they appear satisfied, happy, distraught, or apathetic? Is the facility clean? How would the residents get out in case of fire? Are there enough staff on duty to care for the residents? What activities are going on? Do most residents participate in activities? Are relatives and friends encouraged to visit? Is there a volunteer program at the facility? What kind of food and meal service is provided? What is the general living condition of the nursing home? Is it warm and pleasant or cold and sterile? How would you feel about the possibility of spending the rest of *your* life in this facility?

For a more thorough and comprehensive inspection and evaluation of a nursing home, the group should obtain a consumer checklist or a set of questions and guidelines that have been previously developed by other citizen action groups, HEW, or the American Health Care Association. The Resources section lists some of the better evaluation tools. If your group is really ambitious, you may want to use the federal or state rules and regulations as a basis for evaluation.

Immediately after team members visit the facility, they should prepare a record of both objective and subjective findings and observations for the files. Remember, it will not only be important to document problems, abuses, or any deficiencies you have observed, you will also want to note any special programs or activities that seem to benefit residents.

Conduct a Resident Survey

Traditionally in our agist society older people, especially in institutions, have been subjected to a great deal of paternalism, denied a voice in stating their own needs and wants, and denied a share of the planning and decisionmaking affecting their lives and environment. These people ought to be the most knowledgeable and able to advise health professionals, policy-makers and community members about the kinds of changes necessary and important for improving the quality of life in a nursing home. From the HEW bureaucrat to the man in the street, nearly everyone can tell you what the residents need, so why ask the residents? It is not uncommon to hear someone say, "They don't need anything because they are all happy anyway."

Before a reform program is planned and initiated, your group may want to talk informally with nursing home residents to solicit their views and ideas for programs and services needed to improve the quality of their lives. The information and ideas could be referred to the administrator to encourage the facility to take action. This type of activity is a good way of introducing nursing homes to members of the citizen group who have not had any other experiences with older people in nursing homes.

In fall 1974, the Gray Panther Long-Term Care Action Project developed materials to assist local Gray Panther networks, citizen and church groups in initiating surveys of nursing home residents. Local groups met to discuss the questionnaire and interviewing guidelines to determine what specific types of information they were interested in obtaining. Some group members did role-playing to become familiar with the survey tool and practice interviewing.

The Gray Panther survey was positive in that it did not directly ask "what's wrong" with nursing homes. Rather, the basic intent was to identify (1) what is good about residing in a nursing home, (2) what would make it better, or what would be the "ideal" nursing home. If your group decides to initiate a similar survey, the Gray Panther guidelines and questions which follow may be helpful as you develop your own format.

More than likely you will need to obtain permission to interview residents from the nursing home administrator, nurse-in-charge, or other staff person. Share the questionnaire with this person. Since the survey deals with the positive aspects of institutional living, the staff should be receptive. Offer to share the results of the survey with the facility. Don't be discouraged if you cannot get permission to interview residents in any given nursing home. Just say "thank you" and try another facility, and be sure to note in your file somewhere that a certain nursing home refused to cooperate and record the reasons given.

It would be best if two people conducted the interviews. One should have responsibility for recording the resident's remarks. Try to find a quiet, private area for the interview. Remember to respect the resident's rights. Introduce yourself, the intent and purpose of your visit, and seek his/her permission for visiting and interviewing. You might say something like this: "We're trying to encourage community members to become more involved in improving nursing home life for residents. We believe that when it is necessary for people to live in nursing homes, they should be very good ones. You live in a nursing home, you're really the expert and can tell us what kinds of things would make a nursing home a good place to live. We will share our report with individuals and groups who are concerned or need to be concerned." Tell the resident that his/her name will not be included in any of the survey forms or reports.

The actual interview should be as informal as possible. Ask questions slowly and casually. It is important to remember that *some* nursing home residents have a hearing loss, but *not all*.

Resident Survey Questions

1. "What would you say are the good things, the things you like and find important, about living in a nursing home?" Good things do happen in some nursing homes, and it is important to identify and reinforce those good factors.

2. "If you had all the money and help available to you, and you were to plan and build a new nursing home for your family and friends, what would the home be like? How would it look? What would it be like to live there?" Although somewhat of a fantasy question, it can be fun. Many nursing home residents have very low expectations of what services and rights are actually possible. If given the opportunity to dream about the ideal nursing home for their loved ones, important needs and wants might be expressed.

   Depending on the resident's willingness and ability to answer in detail, you might need to ask only these first two questions. If the resident needs more structure and specific questions, however, the remaining questions might be of help.

3. "What kinds of decisions and choices should you be able to make in a nursing home?" Some residents might ask what you mean by the question and you could respond: "Do you think you should have the freedom to decide what day or what time you take your bath?" or "Would you like to plan the menu and decide on an activity?" Residents should retain some power and control over their lives in a nursing home.

4. "How should you be treated in a nursing home?" This question means how *should* and how *would* they like to be treated. How should personnel address them? Are their knowledge and capabilities recognized and respected? It is important to be treated as an adult and not as a child.

5. "What kinds of things would make you feel safe and secure living in a nursing home?" Safe and secure could mean things such as a quick response to a call for help, staff members who seem to know what they are doing, and a nurse call light always within easy reach.

6. "What kinds of programs, activities, or learning experiences would you like to have?" The resident might say, "Just something to do, I'm so bored." Ask him/her what kinds of things would be important. Ascertain whether there are other experiences, besides an arts and crafts program or a weekly bingo game, that would be of interest. For example,

do they want an up-to-date library or opportunities for continued learning?

7. "What kinds of experiences away from the nursing home are important and should be available to you?" Many residents seldom have an opportunity to leave the nursing home. Do they want to become involved in community affairs, church services, or civic events outside the nursing home? Should transportation be provided?

Study Government Agencies

The public has depended upon government regulatory, inspection, and licensing agencies to promote the public interest and protect the health, safety, and welfare of residents in long-term care facilities. Without local citizen involvement and monitoring, however, a government agency can become stagnant and negligent, resulting in a system of routine bureaucracy and inefficiency. While citizens may not be aware of bureaucratic dealings, industry representatives are usually very knowledgeable since their existence and profits may very well depend on governmental actions (or inactions) that serve their interests.

The primary reason for investigating government agencies is to obtain information which can lead to action. The very presence of citizens, monitoring, asking questions, reviewing documents, can stimulate bureaucracies into action. Citizen attention can greatly enhance an agency's visibility, responsiveness, and, most important, accountability to the public. Citizen involvement of this nature does not require experts in law, government or economics. Any citizens with determination and common sense are quite capable of organizing and conducting an investigation. The investigating team should gather background material dealing with the agency's functions prior to any formal contact or interviews. Information and materials might be obtained directly from the agency, from library reference rooms, legislative records, or from the office of your legislator. Useful background information may include: (1) the legislative bill creating the agency; (2) the agency's rules and regulations; (3) an organizational chart showing the relationships of this particular agency to other agencies; (4) reports, studies, and any other agency publications.

In every agency there is someone who has jurisdiction over each kind of activity. For example, the state department of health will have a director as will the various programs under it, such as division on licensure and inspections, division on medical services, or division on certification. Each state will have different names for each department or division and different titles for the department heads. These names should be identified. You will learn that identifying the correct person for each specific area will usually bring a quicker response to your special requests.

When you feel familiar with the background materials, the group should be ready to proceed with individual interviews with agency personnel. You will need to make an appointment for most interviews, especially for officials in high positions. When requesting an interview, state clearly the purpose of the organization you represent, the purpose of the requested interview, and whether or not you might want any special reports, regulations and/or statistics available for your review during the interview. Once you have stated the purpose and scope of information you are seeking, ask the interviewee if (s)he can suggest any other persons in the department you might benefit from meeting.

Although you will eventually want to meet with the director of a particular agency, it is good to talk with as many agency personnel as possible. Asking the same questions of different individuals can often produce additional or clearer information. Valuable information can also be obtained from former agency personnel. No longer having official allegiance, an ex-employee may feel freer to offer information and critically evaluate the agency.

If officials refuse to meet with you, are uncooperative, or refuse to give information, you should notify in writing your state governor and state attorney general. Then you should tell your story to the press.

Although it is useful to have recordings of special interviews, tape recording is often awkward and intimidating. The person being interviewed may not feel free to give out certain kinds of information while being recorded. It may be a better strategy for two people from your group to attend the interview. One person should have major responsibility for directing the interview while the other takes accurate notes. This also provides two witnesses. To preserve information, notes should be completed and typed for your file as soon after the interview as possible. The group should think the meeting through ahead of time and determine the most important questions that need to be answered. A second interview, especially with the head of an agency, is often difficult to get. Write questions in a notebook and have them readily available.

During the interview you might not ask questions in the order you prepared them. Listening attentively is critical and you must be flexible, ready to follow through with different questions if the need arises. It is a good idea to ask the most important questions several different ways during the course of the interview, making certain that you get the same answers. Naturally you will be concerned about the accuracy. Often the problem is not that you have been given the wrong information, but that it is incomplete. To check for accuracy and honesty, at the beginning of the interview ask a few questions to which you already know the answers. Another useful strategy is to present yourself as being very informed and knowledgeable, even more so than you really may be. This can result in an interviewee's giving you additional facts which might not have been revealed to you. Use an interviewing approach you feel most comfortable with.

Certains questions are essential for studying and evaluating a regulatory agency. The following, which have been adapted from Donald K. Ross' *A Public Citizen's Action Manual,* can serve as a guide when interviewing the director of the agency responsible for licensing and inspecting nursing homes.[1]

1. How many nursing homes does the agency inspect? Are there other institutions or facilities, like home health agencies or hospitals, which the agency inspects?
2. How many inspectors are in the field? How many full time? Part time?
3. How often are inspections *required*?
   The answers to these questions will indicate whether the agency is capable of carrying out its mandate. For example, in Iowa in 1974 there were only ten inspectors in the state department of health with inspection and enforcement responsibilities for 758 facilities.
4. How often are the inspections *actually* made?
5. What are the inspectors' qualifications? What professional disciplines do they represent — registered nurse, pharmacist, etc.?

6. What kinds of special training and/or continuing in-service education is available to inspectors?
7. Have all inspectors attended the federally funded surveyors' (inspectors) training program?
8. Is an inspector responsible for the same facilities all the time, or does a different inspector make each inspection?
9. Are facilities inspected by an individual or a team? If a team, who is on the team?
10. Is the facility notified of the inspection date in advance? If yes, why?
11. What is the inspection procedure? How long does it take?
12. What happens when a nursing home has violations and/or deficiencies?
13. How many deficiencies can a nursing home have and still be considered in compliance?
14. How long does a nursing home have to correct deficiencies?
15. Are follow-up inspections usually made? If so, when?
16. What happens if a deficiency is not corrected in the time allotted?
17. Is information regarding deficient nursing homes available to the public?
18. Where is the very best place for a citizen to obtain information about a particular nursing home and how it meets state standards?
19. To whom should nursing home complaints be directed for the fastest, most effective action?
20. What is the procedure for processing nursing home complaints?

Having obtained this information, your group must now determine the most effective and appropriate way to use it. If the initial goal was background information, you may want to hold the information and incorporate it into your final report. Or, you may want to issue a preliminary report, stating your findings and offering initial recommendations.

Study Laws and Regulations

Some members of the citizen group should be thoroughly familiar with laws and regulations governing nursing homes. Without knowledge of what nursing homes are required to provide, your group will not have a factual, objective basis from which to evaluate existing conditions or plan future actions. For example, the citizen group in Davenport, Iowa, that created the Citizens Monitoring Team, noted that most facilities did not have activity or recreational programs. Recognizing the importance of these programs, the group planned to offer friendly encouragement and assist facilities to establish them. Reading state regulations, the group learned that each facility was *required* to have had an activity program; their strategy of "friendly encouragement" changed to that of standard enforcement.

There are basically three sets of federal laws and state laws and regulations applicable to nursing homes in your community. The legislation for skilled nursing facilities participating in the federal Medicare and Medicaid programs was passed in 1972 and is known as Public Law 92-603. Congress authorized the participation of intermediate care facilities in the Medicaid program in 1972 as Public Law 92-223. Federal laws are compiled in a book called the *United States Code: The Official Edition*, which can be found in the reference section of most large public and university libraries.

Identifying and gaining access to copies of state laws governing nursing home care may be difficult. Most libraries have only the annotated, unofficial editions, for example, *California Code Annotated*. To annotate simply means to comment upon, add notes or place in perspective. Annotated texts can provide historical data, cross-references, and a written commentary covering each law. The best place to find copies of state laws would be the office of the state attorney general or the legislative bureau at the state capital.

It is important to study the laws to determine what the legislature intended. This is difficult since the language is sometimes confusing or quite technical. Study the legislative history of the law, such as transcripts of hearings and committee reports, to determine context and shed light on what the legislators were trying to do by passing the law.

While the legislature passes laws, agencies promulgate regulations. (The term "promulgate," which you will hear often, means to make known, or put into effect, by publishing the terms of the new law.) Regulations are based on laws and are the policy guidelines established to carry out the legislative mandate of the law.

The Social Security Administration is responsible for issuing regulations for skilled nursing and intermediate care facilities participating in the Medicare and Medicaid programs. The regulations have been published in the *Federal Register*, codified in the *Code of Federal Regulations*. The indices and table of contents to these texts should be checked. Specifically, regulations for intermediate care facilities were published in the January 17, 1974 issue of the *Federal Register*, volume 39, number 12, pages 2220 to 2235. Regulations for skilled nursing facilities were published in the *Federal Register*, also on January 17, 1974, volume 39, number 12, pages 2238 to 2257 and on October 3, 1974, volume 39, number 193, pages 35774 to 35778. Copies should be available through the local Social Security Administration, the state health or welfare department, or the HEW regional Office of Long-Term Care Standards Enforcement.

Either the state department of health or welfare will be responsible for issuing state nursing home regulations. The regulations may be scattered in a series of papers rather than in any single document. There may be different sets of regulations for different levels of care. Make sure you have a copy of all applicable regulations. They may be obtained from the nursing home licensure department or the office of the attorney general.

Regulations, though detailed, also tend to be unclear. The language is often vague, ambiguous, using words such as "adequate," "serious," and "sufficient to meet the needs of." This wording can be interpreted in many ways, presenting additional problems for the inspection and enforcement process as well as making it difficult for you to understand what the regulations really intend.

Regulations are usually broken down in subheadings called chapters, titles, or articles. Frequently at the beginning of a chapter there will be a section on definitions. This section should be read carefully since it defines a number of terms (level of care, meaning of "compliance," etc.) used in the remaining part of the chapter. Reading regulations is sometimes boring and confusing. Sentences seem endless, often with qualifications and exceptions that render them almost incomprehensible. It will help if you "brief" the regulations by outlining, underlining, or breaking down component parts in order to see them more clearly.

HEW promulgates "Interpretive Guidelines and Survey Procedures" for Medicare and Medicaid regulations for skilled nursing facilities and intermediate care facilities. These documents are primarily for use of the state survey agency, the state Medicaid agency, providers and organizations, and concerned citizens. The document includes the condition of participation (the regulation), an interpretation of that regulation and suggestions for the nursing home inspector. These guidelines and survey procedures are never considered final and are revised as HEW considers necessary. They serve only as a guide for clarification of standards and are neither laws nor regulations. This information can be very useful to citizen groups attempting to understand the federal regulations and to evaluate nursing homes. "Interpretive Guidelines and Survey Procedures" can be ordered from ONHA, Washington, D.C., or from the HEW regional Office of Long-Term Care Standards Enforcement.

In addition to federal and state regulations, facilities certified for Medicare and Medicaid must also comply with provisions of the Life Safety Code issued by the National Fire Protection Association. The Life Safety Code is a set of fire protection standards covering construction, protection, and occupancy features designed to minimize danger to life from fire, smoke, fumes, or panic. Copies of these standards can be obtained through the health or welfare department or from the office of the state or city fire marshal.

Study Inspection Reports

In every state much criticism has been directed at inadequate nursing home inspection procedures and the lack of standards enforcement. Deficiencies are rarely publicized by state enforcement agencies and only recently have inspection reports been made available for public review.

In most instances the inspection report is the only tool available to the public to (1) determine that inspections have been made, (2) determine the conditions and degree of standards compliance, and (3) determine whether deficiencies have been corrected.

There are five basic inspection reports for Medicare and Medicaid facilities.

1. For skilled nursing facilities, inspection results are recorded on the "Medicare/Medicaid Skilled Nursing Facility

Survey Report" (Form SSA-1569). The 68-page document
lists the full text of each "condition of participation," or individual standard. A "Yes" and "No" checklist indicates whether
or not "individual standards" have been met. Two boxes indicate whether or not the "overall condition" has been "Met" or
"Not Met." Next to the checklist is a column for "Explanatory Statements." If the standard has not been met, the inspector is to explain the nature of the deficiency. In order to determine whether a facility is in compliance with a given condition
of participation, the inspector must decide whether the "intent" of the condition is met. This means that in some cases,
the overall condition will be marked "Met" while individual
standards will not be met. The report form also provides information on ownership, the number of nurses and other personnel, staffing patterns, availability of supportive services, patient
care, and patient activity programs.

2. The inspection report for intermediate care facilities is
called "General Intermediate Care Facility Survey Report"
(Form SSA-3070). Its format is similar to the report for skilled
nursing care facilities.

3. The "Medicare/Medicaid Fire Safety Survey Report"
(Form SSA-2786) is the form used by fire survey authorities
in determining compliance with fire safety standards. The
twelve-page document lists a reference to the Life Safety Code,
rather than the full text of each standard. A checklist indicates
whether the standard has been met or not met, with space for
explanatory remarks. If any items are marked "Not Met," the
facility can only be in compliance if the certifying authority
grants a waiver or accepts a plan of correction for unwaivered
deficiencies. The report has three parts. Part I is the guide to
surveying for compliance with the code. Part II lists those fire
safety requirements of Medicare and Medicaid not contained
in the Life Safety Code, and Part III contains a certification
form to be completed by the state fire authority when waiver
of a specific provision is recommended.

4. The "Statement of Deficiency and Plan of Correction"
(Form SSA-2567), sometimes called "The Summary of Deficiencies," is prepared by the inspector at the conclusion of the
inspection. This form has two purposes: (1) It serves as the
correction plan required for acceptance or renewal of the provider agreement and (2) it is the vehicle for disclosing deficiency information to the public. For each standard marked "Not

Met," the surveyor makes an entry on the left-hand column of the form. The entry lists the deficiency and the specific regulatory section number of the standard not met. An asterisk placed by any deficiency signifies a waiver recommendation. Provisions waived are not considered deficiencies. The form is sent to the provider within ten days of the inspection. The provider enters his responses which must include his proposed action to remedy the deficiency, the expected completion date, and whether or not any deficiencies have already been corrected. For each deficiency listed, there must be a plan of correction marked on the right-hand column. The provider has ten days to return this form to the regulatory agency.

5. The "Post-Certification Revisit Report" (Form SSA-2567B) is completed by the inspector to report the status of deficiencies reported on Form SSA-2567 described above. If the deficiency has not been entirely corrected, the inspector must indicate whether the facility has made "substantial effort and progress." Where substantial progress has been made but corrections have not been completed, a new plan of correction on Form SSA-2567 must be obtained from the administrator.

The Freedom of Information Act as well as a 1972 provision in the Social Security Act established the right of public access to nursing home inspection reports on file in any federal agency or department. In 1972 after unsuccessfully requesting inspection reports for various nursing homes, plaintiffs in three states and the District of Columbia filed lawsuits challenging the Secretary of HEW's authority to withhold the reports as violations of both the Freedom of Information Act and the purposes of the Social Security Act. After the cases were filed, Congress amended the Medicare law and specifically required the Secretary of HEW to make Medicare inspection information available through its 1,200 district offices. The Medicaid program must make its inspection information available through local public welfare offices. The law requires that both the summaries and full inspection reports be available to the public no later than ninety days following the inspection. It further stipulates that public disclosure is required only for reports prepared after January 31, 1973.

It is important to note that these two acts allow for disclosure of inspection reports only for skilled and intermediate care facilities participating in either the Medicare or Medicaid reimbursement program. Some nursing homes do not participate in either program. However, all nursing homes, regardless of whether they participate in federal programs, must be licensed by the state regulatory agency. Each state will vary, but some like California, Iowa, and Minnesota, have enacted legislation allowing for disclosure.

Your group will need to find out whether your state statutes provide for public disclosure. Call your state licensing agency or attorney general's office and ask. If you are told they do not, ask for the exact state law or regulations which stipulate this policy.

In implementing the Freedom of Information Act and congressional mandate, the Social Security Administration chose to interpret the new provisions very narrowly. As a result, only the summary reports, the Statement of Deficiencies and Plan of Correction and the Post-Certification Revisit Report forms are available at the local Social Security or public assistance office. To obtain these reports, visit the local office and ask for the reports by facility name. No written request is necessary. If ninety days have passed since the inspection, summary reports should be on file in the local office and available to you.

The full inspection reports (Forms SSA-1569, SSA-3070, and SSA-2786) may be obtained by submitting a written request to the district Social Security or public assistance office which should forward your request to the appropriate state or regional office. (Guidelines for requesting information under the Freedom of Information Act are described at the beginning of this chapter.)

Local staff may not be aware that inspection reports are public information. Do not accept a reply that they are confidential. The only information that should be confidential is the names of nursing home residents and they will not appear on inspection forms. You do not have to explain the reason for your request and government employees do not have the right to ask. If you have difficulty with the local offices, take a copy of the regulations with you. The regulations about public access to Medicare/Medicaid inspection reports may be found in the *Federal Register*, May 10, 1974, volume 39, no. 92, page 16973; and July 23, 1974, volume 39, no. 142, page 26722. If your request for a Medicare/Medicaid inspection report has been denied, write immediately or call the HEW regional director of the Office of Long-Term Care Standards Enforcement.

Study the Health Systems Agency

The National Health Planning and Resources Development Act passed in 1974 is meant to result in a national health planning and resources development system. This network will replace existing regional medical programs and comprehensive health planning agencies. It will also replace the Hill-Burton hospital and nursing home construction program with a program for the modernization and building of medical and long-term care facilities. The law requires that state governors designate health service areas in their states. Within each of these areas a Health System Agency (HSA) will be organized and funded by HEW.

Existing public nonprofit and private corporations may be designated as HSAs. The HSA must have a governing board of ten to thirty members, the majority of whom must be consumers and the remainder providers. Board members must be residents of the health service area and must include elected officials as well as other government representatives who may be either consumers or providers.

The HSAs will be responsible for: (1) preparing long-range health system plans; (2) assisting states in reviewing the needs for both new and existing health, mental health, and long-term care services; (3) reviewing all institutional health and long-term care services offered; and (4) making recommendations to the state agency regarding the appropriateness of such facilities.

Each state is to designate a unit as the state planning and development agency. These will coordinate the health plans of the local HSAs into statewide plans, review the appropriateness of institutional health services, and establish a certificate of need program for health and long-term care services. Each state health planning and development agency must be advised by a statewide health coordinating council, composed of consumers, government representatives, and providers.

In many areas the establishment of HSAs has been quite controversial. It has been a struggle to make sure that consumers who *actually represent community health interests* are involved as board members. Since there is a clear mandate for including "special consumer" interests, there is no reason why nursing home residents and certainly members of nursing home reform groups cannot be legitimate representatives of those needing long-term care.

The hearings of the planning and development agencies around the country are open to the public, providing a good opportunity for citizen groups to raise questions and give their views about pending applications.

A review of state nursing home association newsletters over the past year has shown that the industry is focusing a considerable amount of attention on HSAs — strongly encouraging and promoting local industry involvement. The industry is obviously fearful of the possibility of strong controls HSAs might have over the entire nursing home industry.

Study the Power Structure and Special Interests

In order to hold someone accountable for poor living conditions, it is necessary to determine who actually owns the nursing homes in the community. In many cases true ownership can only be identified through vigilant power-structure research. Nursing home administrators must be licensed, but not nursing home owners. The nursing home operator, the person or company doing business, must also be identified, but not the owners. The owner(s) plays a most important role in major decisionmaking, collects most of the profits, yet may not even have any direct contact with the facility, the staff, or the residents and their families.

As we've noted, Medicare and Medicaid regulations do require that each facility participating in either federal program disclose its ownership, those owning ten percent or more. This information is obtained during the facility's inspection and is recorded on the survey report (Form SSA-1569 and SSA-3070), which is available for public review. The disclosure of ownership standard requires the facility to identify the following: (1) each person who has any direct or indirect ownership interest of ten percent or more, or the owner of any mortgage, deed of trust, note, or other obligation secured or any property or other assets of the facility; (2) if the facility is organized as a corporation, each officer and director must be identified by name and address as well as those stockholders holding more than ten percent.

While this information may be valuable, it has not provided sufficient information about nursing home ownership. For example, several members of one family can each own stock under the ten percent figure and thereby have control while concealing true ownership.

A further benefit of power-structure research is to identify possible conflict of interest, vested interest, or weak points in the system. This knowledge gives a citizen group a handle to challenge the system effectively. When pieced together with other findings, sometimes even an apparently insignificant finding can have great implications. For example, the citizen group in Davenport, Iowa, could not understand how the "worst" facilities in the county were always relicensed following inspection. After doing research in the county courthouse, it was learned that the agent for the corporation owning those "worst" facilities was the husband of the inspector.

The public image and trust of a local physician can be important to his continued respect and prosperity. Patients and relatives might get an "enlightened" impression if, through power-structure research, they learned that their doctor had a concealed financial stake in the facility he recommended. Another example of "enlightenment" that is not uncommon, is to discover a state health or welfare department official or state legislator or other elected official who is an owner or has a significant amount of nursing home stock.

If your citizen group needs only to research who owns the nursing home on Fourth and Main, or if the group should decide to do a complete ownership study of all nursing homes in the state, the basic "how-to" elements are essentially the same. The first point to remember is the public has a right to the information discussed in this section, a right guaranteed by law. A second basic principle: information is only valuable if it is documented. The research team should keep an accurate record of what was found and where it was located. Remember, the entire investigation can be discounted because of only one piece of incorrect information.

The county courts administer the majority of state judicial systems so the investigation should begin in the county courthouse. Most people are unaware of the magnitude of public information stored there, which includes land titles, liens, mortgages, tax records, corporation books; birth, marriage, and divorce records; estates and wills; and the proceedings of criminal and civil court actions.

If you begin with area nursing homes, your investigator will need a list of the names and addresses of the facilities. The best list can be obtained from the state licensure agency.

Beginning at the real estate tax office, you can find the nursing home's physical location on the "block and lot" number map. The corresponding books then list the person who gets the tax bills, and if different, the individual actually paying the property taxes. It should be noted that neither of those listed individuals is necessarily the property owner. For your information, record the assessed property value, the amount of tax billed and paid, and who paid the taxes.

The local building department will sometimes provide useful information regarding nursing home property. Filed under the block and lot number are copies of all documents involving land improvements and building construction. Building inspection reports are also filed and available for public review.

The next step is to go to the county clerk's office where there will be a series of books indexed according to address. You can find the following: (1) the date the facility was established or bought; (2) who sold it; (3) who bought it; and (4) the volume and page numbers of the corporation books.

You can find information on nursing homes owned or operated by corporations as well as those privately owned in the corporation books in the county recorder's office. Information in these books includes: (1) the name and address of the owner or president; (2) the date the facility was acquired; (3) the name of the corporation and the location of the main office; (4) whether the corporation has a profit or nonprofit status; (5) the number of shares sold; (6) the names of the major stockholders; (7) a listing of any restrictions on the transfer of shares; (8) the name and address of the agent; (9) the names and addresses of the board of directors; and (10) the dates and locations of the board meetings.

Information in the initial corporation books is not always complete and you may be referred to other corporation and miscellaneous books which contain: (1) current information on ownership and mergers; (2) transactions initiated by the corporation to purchase other facilities or other types of businesses; (3) change of address of the main office; (4) any change in the agent; (5) any sale of equipment, etc., either inside the facility or on the property; and (6) a list of any forfeitures and the reasons a forfeit occurred. Because you want current information, all references and referrals to other sources should be explored.

The land deed and mortgage books are usually found in the same room in the courthouse. The land deed book lists: (1) the owner of the property; (2) a detailed description of the location and boundaries of the property. The mortgage records are divided into two parts; the first part is called the mortgage grantor-grantee index. You need to know the name of the facility and the date of purchase and the index will then indicate which mortgage book you want for further information. The index contains information on: (1) the property currently providing income and (2) the amount of sale and the terms of payment. The second part will provide information on (1) the property bought and the terms of payment; (2) the sale price and (3) the name of the seller.

The procedure for investigating individuals is similar to that for facilities and can usually begin with the city directory. Most cities have an annual city directory; copies are usually found in city hall and the public library. The directory is categorized in three parts, by name, address, and telephone number. Information includes: (1) the spouse's name; (2) the occupation of the head of the household; (3) whether the individual is a director, officer or employee of a corporation and (4) names of family members living at that address. Remember, you are looking for bits of information that might seem unimportant alone, but pieced with other information, might be very significant.

Back at the county courthouse, look through the city and county tax records for the individual. There are two sets of books; property and personal property tax records. The property records will state: (1) the amount of property owned; (2) the assessed value of the property; (3) the value of any building and land improvements; and (4) whether there are any delinquent taxes and the amount. The personal property tax records vary from state to state. For instance, in some states, the records list only information about automobile ownership while other states list bank accounts, stocks, and information on many other assets. Investigation of personal property may

be very significant to your campaign. It is hard to sympathize with a nursing home owner who says he makes no profits on his nursing home business and cannot afford to hire a social worker for his residents when you know he buys a new Cadillac every year, lives in a $75,000 home, and owns a lakefront cottage.

A major trend in nursing home ownership is ownership by corporations with large chain operations. While researching a corporation, the fundamental questions are who are the officers and directors and who owns and controls the corporation? Investigation of corporate involvements should begin in the reference section of most college and city libraries. *Poor's Registry of Executives and Directors*, indexed alphabetically, lists over thirty thousand large and middle-sized corporations. Also listed are the names of the managers and directors with brief individual biographies noting all their board positions.

The Securities and Exchange Commission (SEC), a federal regulatory agency, supervises all public bond and stock offerings and requires some corporations to submit reports on their financial operations. To determine if the corporation under investigation is required to file reports, check the *Directory of Corporation Filing with the Securities and Exchange Commission*. The *Directory* lists the stock owned by officers and directors and includes a partial listing of major stockholders.

Federal laws also require that a report be filed with the SEC every time stocks are bought or sold. This information is obtained from the monthly *Official Summary of Security Transactions and Holdings*. Indexed alphabetically by corporation name, it lists who made the transaction, the date of the transaction, and the amount of stock owned by the individual after the transaction was made. By reviewing back issues of the *Official Summary* you can obtain a fairly complete listing of stockholders, and you can also evaluate the economic status of the corporation. A complete investigation of stockholders is vital if your goal is to discover any possible relationships between corporations and other corporations or between individuals and several corporations.

If your group is investigating lawyers and/or judges, a good source of information located in the public library is the *Martindale-Hubell Law Directory*, which lists lawyers by states, cities, and law firms and contains educational background, a list of corporate clients, and sometimes the person's estimated net worth. The *Directory of American Judges* may also be helpful, for it lists judges both alphabetically and geographically and contains brief biographies.

After completing these investigatory procedures, a fairly clear picture of nursing home ownership and any other special interest forces will become apparent. Even then, however, you will probably have seen only the tip of the iceberg.[2]

PLANNING, PUBLICIZING, AND
LOBBYING

The most important thing the reader should know about citizen action is that it can work. It has worked. It is working. The next most important thing is that enthusiasm is not enough. If citizen action is to be successful, it requires careful preparation through the development of strategies and the utilization of available resources.

Strategy simply means the necessary planning, direction and activities to achieve your goals. It involves identifying resources and developing the means to use them effectively. Since the course of every citizen action campaign depends on a number of variables — the issues, targets, the political climate, the degree of organization — there is no one method for organizing a campaign. But there are common strategies and resources that have direct application to most citizen groups. They are described in this chapter.

Planning for Action

After completing the initial education, research, and investigative activities, analyze your findings. What are the real nursing home problems in your community? Does a general pattern of problems or deficiencies emerge? How serious are they? Is an obvious issue the lack of consumer information about community facilities or is the problem lack of enforcement by the health department?

The issue you select should be an obvious felt need — clearly defined and manageable. The selection of an issue depends not only on the issue itself. Consider the knowledge and experiences of the group. Is the issue abstract or is it something people can grasp easily? Is it an issue group members believe they can do something about?

A common weakness among novice citizen groups is tackling too many broad issues, failing to work on concrete, tangible, and achievable goals. Citizen action scattered in all directions changes little. It has not been uncommon for citizen groups to select and try to act not only on the entire nursing home reform issue but on alternatives to institutionalization as well.

Nursing home reform encompasses a *wide* range of issues, any one of which could be a major project. Depending on your own organizational resources, a workable issue, for example, could be the lax enforcement system, the lack of activity and socialization programs, or the lack of medical care and supervision.

There is no question about the necessity of advocating effective alternatives to institutionalization. No doubt as your group begins organizing, you will frequently hear, "Now, if you *really* want to do something, work for alternatives." Alternatives are a distinctly separate issue. Unless your active membership is large enough to tackle two action projects, it is best to choose one or the other. Do not allow others to divert the group from your selected agenda. In fact, if your group is working on the nursing home issue and you begin hearing, " . . . if you really want to do something . . . " it probably means your actions are beginning to be effective.

After selecting issues, establish priorities and a time frame for achieving each step. Outline your program in a clear, concise manner:

- State your long-term and short-term goals.

- List specific actions necessary to accomplish the goals.

- Establish priorities for action.

- Establish a realistic timetable for accomplishing each action and goal.

Be realistic about your goals and timetable. For example, the passage of legislation creating a fining and citation system took almost two years from the time the Iowa Student Public

Interest Research Group uncovered enforcement system problems.

ISPIRG's long-term goal had been to upgrade nursing homes by instituting a fining and citation system. An intermediate goal was to find a sympathetic legislator to introduce the bill. Prior to reaching that however, there were many short-term goals and actions. For example, the group had to obtain information on the current regulatory and enforcement system. It involved: obtaining a copy of the current licensure law and regulations, a list of all licensed nursing homes, and a list of the nursing home inspectors; interviewing department of health personnel, reviewing inspection reports, and visiting nursing homes.

Using the Media

The media can be a powerful tool for spreading the word about nursing home issues, enlisting the support of citizens and groups, and applying pressure on government and industry.

Successful use of publicity calls for deliberate efforts on the part of one or more members to learn how to deal with the media.

Inexperienced citizen groups have not always benefited from media coverage. Premature exposure can sometimes be counterproductive. Too much publicity when you are not ready for it can be as difficult as too little when you really need it. Do not let the media take advantage of you, and do not seek media attention until you are ready for it. Another word of caution: successful publicity does not make a successful organization. A good news story about you or your group is no substitute for the basic job of organizing the community around the issue of nursing home reform.

There are basically four types of reporters, all with some overlapping areas of responsibility. Investigative reporters usually handle special assignments requiring extensive research. The general assignment reporter may specialize in special issues, such as health care, but generally does a little of everything. The beat reporter covers special places, such as city hall or the state legislature. The feature writer handles special topics, detailing background information, discussing theory, and often editorializing.

Maintain a news clipping file on all items about long-term care — often a good assignment for group members unable to leave their homes. Which reporters are writing what kinds of stories? Who may be sympathetic to your concern? You may be successful in getting an investigative reporter to do an in-depth series of articles. If so, assist this person with background information and any special tips or leads you might have.

The news release and the news conference are tools frequently used by citizen action groups. If your membership does not include a person experienced in writing news releases, seek advice from the editor or reporters of the local newspaper, a school of journalism, or from an organization or consumer group with successful media experience. Ask for specifics on format and how to present content.

The "lead" paragraph is most important. In three or four lines it should state who did what, when, where, how, and sometimes why. For example, "Creation of a city ordinance requiring stricter inspection procedures for boarding homes and the publication of a consumer directory of care homes in Davenport were recommended today in the final report submitted to Mayor Kathryn Kirschbaum by the Citizens Monitoring Team."

Organize a press conference when you have something especially significant to announce like the formation of your action group, the findings of your investigation, or the presentation of a report or special recommendations.

Unless it is an emergency, prepare several days in advance by writing and distributing a short press release. For example: "Charles Chomet, Executive Director of Citizens for Better Care, will hold a press conference on May 10 at 10:00 A.M. at the organization's headquarters, 960 Jefferson. Chomet and CBC's legal counsel will announce plans to initiate litigation with the State Health Department for its alleged failure to enforce patient rights regulations."

Several hours prior to the conference call the editors, reporters, or the assignment desks, reminding them of the conference, the place and time, and ask whether or not someone will attend.

Prepare a "press packet" containing the complete text of the statement, any relevant background materials and biographical information on any speaker. The statement should be short and highlight the issues or findings. It may be good to prepare a brief press release summarizing the statement. Neither the press packet nor the contents of the statement should be given to any reporter before the conference; maintain your credibility by giving all editors simultaneous access to the material. The packets should also be distributed to media representatives not in attendance.

Have an articulate, confident, and knowledgeable group spokesperson read the prepared text and open the conference to questions. Other group members can sit with the spokesperson and assist in answering questions. Good preconference planning includes anticipating possible questions and preparing concise, factual, and solid answers. Have supporting documents or evidence available. Present statistical evidence on a chart or other visual aids for emphasis.

A word of caution: a press conference is your time with the media and you must use it effectively. If the conference pertains to the discussion or exposé of controversial materials, do not invite your opponents. You run the risk of having your conference turn into an open debate and attention will be diverted from your agenda.

Fear of a lawsuit sometimes prevents groups from either using the media or from naming specific individuals and facilities in a negative way. Reporters are out to get a "good story" and very often ask leading questions such as: "Which is the worst nursing home in the community?" Perhaps the best response is to give the reporter information from which he or she can draw conclusions. For example, you might say: "We are concerned about these facilities because they have only a conditional license and these documented deficiencies. While other community facilities have patient activity programs and an effective volunteer program, these homes do not." Avoid name-calling and making unsubstantiated charges and accusations. Be sure your intellect, not your emotions, is in command. If your information is documented, factual, and accurate, you should not fear a lawsuit. If you have any questions about possible libelous statements, seek help from community legal services.

News stories may go through four to six different individuals before they are actually printed or reported on TV. Be prepared to find your story not quite like you told it.

The first time you are misquoted or your statements misrepresented can be a frightening experience. Accept it as par for the course. It is important to remember when speaking to the media to be clear, specific, and brief. When possible have written statements available. If a serious factual error occurs, make a written request for a retraction or correction. If the misquoted statement involves an individual, agency, or institution, write a letter to the editor with the appropriate correction. Send a carbon copy to the parties involved.

Look beyond newspapers, radio, and television for publicity resources. Use the public library to compile a list of any publications of government agencies, professional, trade, and voluntary associations. Many senior citizen groups, nutrition centers, and community and civic organizations publish newsletters. Delegate a group member to write or call the organizations to learn if they accept stories, announcements, or news items from other than their immediate constituencies. If they do, get their guidelines and publication deadlines.

Getting Legal Help

In nursing home reform work many citizens have to learn to interpret laws and regulations. Many of the issues faced are legal; many of the problems to be resolved involve action that has legal ramifications. Citizen groups are frequently in contact with attorneys in legislative work. They are often asked to help analyze and even to draft legislation. This is challenging, but for many it can take time and special effort to become comfortable with these aspects of reform work.

Attorneys can provide valuable services to help citizens achieve their program goals. It is important to become aware of how they can be of help and how and where they can be found.

Legal Services Programs. Most larger communities have Legal Services programs established to aid the poor. These programs can often provide assistance on nursing home issues. For example, the Denver Metropolitan Legal Aid Society has been active in litigation to protect the rights of nursing home patients. The Senior Citizens' Law Center, part of the Denver program, received a grant from HEW to administer the state nursing home ombudsman grant.

A few states, such as Pennsylvania and Michigan, have a statewide back-up center for legal service programs which engage solely in research, technical assistance, and legislative work, often on issues affecting older people.

Private Attorneys and Bar Associations. Local and state bar associations may assist you. For example, the Arlington County (Virginia) Bar Association joined citizen groups to persuade the county to allow the building of a nursing home because none existed in the area. Some bar associations have organized panels of attorneys who work on problems of older people. Bar associations usually run referral services, which put you in touch with panel members, individual attorneys, or firms which offer *pro bono* (nonpaid) services to community groups.

Law Schools. Citizen groups should not hesitate to approach law schools to solicit assistance from law professors and law students working under lawyer supervision. The University of Pennsylvania Law School's Health Law Project has worked extensively with community groups active in nursing home reform. They have published some excellent materials on legal problems and organizing in nursing homes. Their work on citizen access to nursing homes was the basis for the access regulations adopted in Pennsylvania. Among law schools now specializing in legal problems of the elderly are George Washington University in Washington, D.C.; Duke University in Durham, North Carolina; the University of Michigan in Ann Arbor; and Syracuse University in Syracuse. In New Hampshire the state agency on aging chose Franklin Pierce Law School to operate the state nursing ombudsman project.

Paralegals. Similar to the low-cost, high-value skills of law students are those of paralegals. Paralegals (sometimes called legal assistants) usually work under attorney supervision. They have basic legal skills in research, interviewing, investigation and negotiation and are able to represent clients in administrative hearings. They can be valuable in working on nursing home issues. For example a VISTA paralegal with Seattle Legal Services has investigated and resolved individual complaints, worked on better enforcement of state standards, presented testimony in official hearings, and has developed a nursing home legal manual. In California elderly paralegals employed by Legal Services established a nursing home referral service hotline.

Paralegals can be effective advocates for residents. Among other activities, they can help draft wills, represent residents at administrative hearings on Social Security and other public benefits, monitor the enforcement of residents' rights, and help mobilize and organize resident councils and grievance procedures in nursing homes.

Paralegals are often employed by legal service programs such as the Denver Legal Aid ombudsman project. Funds for paralegal positions can come from special sources such as Title IX of the Older Americans Act or the Comprehensive Employment and Training Act of 1973 (CETA). In some communities, volunteers from RSVP and VISTA serve as paralegals after receiving special training. If you are incorporated and have a nonprofit status, you may be eligible to sponsor these types of workers, particularly if you can enlist an attorney to supervise the paralegal's work.

Other Resources. Attorneys from a state attorney general's office often become involved in special nursing home investigations and action. The attorney general can bring charges or assist in prosecuting any nursing home criminal violation. In San Jose, California, the Santa Clara Valley Coalition persuaded the state attorney general and the local district attorney to conduct special investigations based on the preliminary research and complaint gatherings of the coalition's nursing home task force. In Los Angeles, the city attorney's office issued a special report and recommendations for nursing home reform.

Attorneys serving as staff for state legislators are often available to assist citizen groups in drafting legislation or in obtaining valuable resource information. Local and state consumer protection agencies often employ attorneys or have staff experts who have special legal skills and knowledge of the law.

In a few states, attorneys, law students, and other specialists work in public interest research groups such as those begun by Ralph Nader. Special research and investigation has resulted in nursing home reports and activities by the Connecticut, Iowa, Maine and Oregon Public Interest Research Groups. They are effective in monitoring government agency activities and in promoting enforcement of the law as well as working for progressive nursing home legislation.

What Special Assistance Can Attorneys Provide?

Attorneys can help research particularly complex complaints or patterns of abuses, analyze problem situations to ascertain whether violations of law are present, and represent residents.

An attorney may be helpful on common problems such as
access to nursing homes, liability of citizen groups which publish evaluations or ratings of facilities, confidentiality of both
complaints and records, access to governmental inspection reports, or the validity of nursing home contracts. An attorney
can help develop a sound complaint form or assist in collecting
evidence for state hearings on certification, decertification, or
licensure. In California, Leslie Kwass, an attorney with the
California Rural Legal Assistance program, developed a guide
to help citizens file complaints about nursing homes.

When difficult or complex problems arise, attorneys can
help put facts in perspective and identify courses of action.
They might suggest litigation on any number of grounds including a nursing home's negligence; violations of federal, state, or
local law or regulations; abuse of individual constitutional or
civil rights; or violation of a contract.

An attorney's action could result in increased publicity,
recovery of monetary damages, access to a facility, an end to
particular patient abuses, decertification of a home, fines
against a home, the stopping of state Medicaid payments,
interference with a proposed patient relocation, forced compliance with the Life Safety Code, placing a home in receivership,
disclosure of records and reports, or any number of other possibilities.

You might persuade your local bar association or individual
attorneys to assist you in interpreting and promoting patients'
rights in nursing homes. For example, in celebration of "D.C.
Law Day 1975" District of Columbia bar association members
visited twenty local program and housing sites for the elderly,
including five nursing facilities, to give talks on the legal rights
of residents.

Many legal services projects for the elderly have developed
books or pamphlets on legal rights and benefits available to
older people, suitable for distribution to patients and families
or suitable for use by citizens involved in nursing home reform
work.

Legislation. Citizen groups usually find they need an attorney to help analyze, draft, and testify for nursing home legislation. For example, a law school professor, John J. Regan, con-
sulting with Legal Research and Services for the Elderly,
drafted Maryland's patients' bill of rights, which was adopted
in 1975. Lawyers with California Rural Legal Assistance

drafted and followed through the legislative process exemplary legislation creating a state citation and fine enforcement system.

It is obvious that public-spirited, knowledgeable attorneys can provide valuable assistance. In addition, they can add "visible clout" in promoting the goals of your work. It is clear, however, that much of the knowledge and many of the skills lawyers offer are not unique to their profession. Several successful citizen groups have worked closely with attorneys and the legal process and have developed their own "legal" expertise in the process. They are now effective at legal research, interviewing, investigation, negotiation, interpreting laws and regulations, and helping others draft legislation. They have learned to recognize when they really need legal advice and direct legal assistance.

Your group may be able to find a Legal Services attorney, law professor, or private attorney who will meet with you in several sessions designed to teach advocacy skills, legal issues, and legal action for nursing home reform.

Now that major investigations are being conducted around the country by attorneys who have joined the impetus for reform, the nursing home industry has become even more sensitized to its need for legal help. It is not uncommon to see special seminars on legal issues and action advertised in state industry newsletters.

Lobbying For Legislative and Administrative Reform

In its simplest form, lobbying is asking for help from people in decisionmaking positions. The basic aim is to urge or secure passage (or defeat) of a bill or regulation. Lobbying can influence legislative or administrative agency priorities, or the time frame in which action is taken. For example, it may be important to get a legislative committee to delay action on a bill until you have essential public and political backing. Or it may be necessary to lobby for an extension in time for public comment on regulations issued by regulatory agencies.

Nearly every citizen group finds it necessary to upgrade or replace existing state nursing home laws and their companion rules and regulations. Sometimes the legislative world is completely foreign to consumers. Those groups are fortunate which have members who know how the legislative and regulatory system works.

The nursing home industry in most states and certainly at the national level is well organized to lobby for its interests. There is an association in each state, usually located in the state capital. It is either staffed with an experienced lobbyist or the association contracts with a lobbying firm. Members are well aware that the largest part of their membership is used for lobbying. The fees run from $100 upward per year and it is not unusual for the association to levy special taxes on the membership when "extra" efforts are needed to influence those in power.

Many citizen groups described in Part Three have lobbied successfully. The Iowa Student Public Interest Research Group (ISPIRG) was the major lobbying arm for some of the most progressive nursing home legislation in the nation. The group started from scratch, learning about the legislative process and what they could do to affect it. In Kansas, the executive secretary of Kansans for the Improvement of Nursing Homes (KINH) registered in the state capital as a lobbyist. The following ideas in this section come directly from what ISPIRG, KINH, and other citizen groups have learned.

Citizen groups should use every tool, technique, and strategy to the advantage of their constituents. There is no mysterious force which makes things happen at city hall: the system will differ from state to state. No group should hold fast to any set rules for lobbying. But we hope the guidelines in the following pages prove useful to individuals and groups who have not yet experienced the confusing and baffling network known as the legislative system.

Finding a Supportive Legislator

If you have selected legislative reform as a priority and have decided what legislative action you want to promote, find a legislator who will support your program.

If your governor has a good track record for seeing that his programs get support from the legislature, start with the governor's office. Seek his or his aides' help to find a legislator to introduce your proposal. You will have some assurance that the governor will sign the bill if it is passed, and his influence and staff may help in the legislative process.

The best legislator would be one who is sympathetic to

your views, or could be persuaded to be; holds an important position in the legislature, such as majority leader; is a member or a chairman of an important committee; has a good record for getting bills passed; has a history of seeking ideas and technical assistance from consumer groups; has shown concern for the elderly and for improved health care; has a good record for fighting for the bills (s)he introduced.

It will be hard to find someone will all these qualifications, but it is worth a try. It is not uncommon for a group to place its faith in someone who has introduced a good bill only to learn that the person stopped action after the first visible gesture of support.

Some good sources of information about legislators may be the director of your local area agency or commission on aging, the director of a local senior center or nutrition program for the elderly, members of the League of Women Voters, a newspaper reporter who covers legislative issues or health or consumer affairs, or a local community action program or consumer organization. Most states have health and welfare associations that are independent of government agencies though their membership may include government employees. These associations often (but not always) work for progressive changes. They usually have a legislative committee whose members may have special insights about legislators and the state legislative process.

When you find legislators who may be supportive, arrange to meet them at their earliest convenience. Tell them about your concerns, goals, and activities. If possible, provide brief, factual, written materials describing your group and its aims.

If you have formulated ideas for legislation, offer a one- to two-page summary of what you would propose. The summary should include: why a bill or amendment is needed; how it would supplement or correct existing legislation; and what organizations support the proposal.

Keep your initial contact brief and to the point. Do not push the legislator for any commitment. You may want to visit several representatives before you decide who would be best to introduce legislation you want passed.

Strategies for Lobbying: A Checklist

1. Study how a bill becomes law. Ordinarily you can obtain

basic printed information from your governor's office or the office of the state attorney general. Have someone experienced in the legislative process talk to your group to give you special information which may not be in print. A Legal Services attorney or an experienced lobbyist from another citizen action group would be helpful.

2. Determine the timing considerations for introducing bills. Does a bill have to be introduced by a specific date to be considered by a certain committee? How long is the legislature in session?

3. Learn the proper procedures for lobbying. Even if your group decides not to lobby immediately, you will be able to observe the process. Seek advice from other lobbyists who might support your work. Find out exactly who lobbies for the industry.

4. Get a list of the legislature's standing committees, and a list of all elected representatives with addresses and phone numbers. Find out which committees are responsible for nursing home issues. Write to the clerks of the house and the senate for this information.

5. If you are not already familiar with the state capitol complex, arrange for a tour for your group so you will know where to go for certain materials and information. Where is the bill room? The library? The committee offices and hearing rooms? The press room? Get to know the place so you won't spend needless time looking for a room when time is precious. Besides, you'll be more impressive as a group if you look as if you know exactly where you are going.

6. After you determine what committee deals with nursing home legislation, review available minutes or records documenting the committee's record in handling previous issues. What were their comments and questions? Maybe you can have some answers in advance of their questions this year.

7. Do research on committee legislators who will review the bill. What is their voting history? Do any of them share ownership in a nursing home or related business? Which are friendly with the industry? Which have received campaign donations from industry members? Which will be sympathetic to your work? Which will need a lot of education or attention to win them over?

8. Obtain copies of innovative well-written legislation from other states relating to the issues you deal with.

9. Seek experienced persons to help you draft a bill. Legislative staff and attorney allies, particularly those who work in Legal Services offices can take your ideas and produce a bill. Most states have a legislative service bureau which will help prepare a proper draft for any legislator.

Ask to see each draft since it will probably be revised several times. Make sure it continues to say what you want or has been strengthened rather than weakened. Check the final version with your allies, an attorney, and anyone else knowledgeable about legislation. Make sure there are no loopholes or unforeseen consequences that would actually hurt your constituents. Find time to go over the bill in detail with the legislators who sponsor the bill so you can be sure they understand it.

10. Build a coalition of support from individuals and organizations around the state. Send letters to influential people such as the head of the state office on aging and area offices on aging. Keep them informed of your progress and let them know when you need their help.

11. Meet with committee legislators individually to present your views and to provide educational materials. If your own elected representative is not a member of the committee, you may want to meet with and advise him/her of your actions and concerns. Ask for assistance in getting support from committee members.

12. Keep a written record of every meeting you have with a legislator, staff person, or committee. It takes time, but it's worth it. You need to document what people have said they will endorse, oppose, or change. Be sure to answer any requests for information. It's always good to have at least two people present at each meeting so this task can be shared and information authenticated.

13. Always have enough copies of materials to be able to give each legislator a copy. When writing letters of request or letters seeking information, send copies to all committee members as well as the chairperson.

14. Use experts from within and outside the state. Arrange for them to meet the legislator(s) or staff person(s) working with you.

15. Lobby for public hearings on the bill. If hearings are scheduled, you will definitely want to testify. Recommend other groups or experts who will testify in support of the bill.

Do not hesitate to request to testify at legislative hearings if you are not asked. If you enter the process too late to testify, ask the committee to accept a formal written statement for the record. Copies of this testimony should be given directly to each member of the committee. Follow up to see that it is read, since attention paid to such material after the hearing could be minimal.

16. Visit or write the editors of the major newspapers in your state as well as the local papers, to inform them of reforms you are seeking. Give them brief educational materials. If they have a special reporter working on legislative issues and/or nursing home affairs, contact that reporter. Keep all informed of special hearings, votes, etc.

17. Invite appropriate legislators to attend a meeting of your group. Attend meetings at which they are speaking. Ask serious questions about nursing home issues and their views on reform. It is harder for an elected official to say no or disagree in a public gathering. Record what each has said and hold them accountable for their public pronouncements.

18. You will probably need to be at the capitol building at least once every two weeks throughout the legislative session — more often as your bill gets to the floor. Keep in constant touch with what's happening. Don't let an important meeting or session slip by. It could be disastrous. The industry will always be there.

19. From the beginning, seek support from the state agencies that will be administering the law. It can be disastrous if they disapprove of the proposed law in public.

20. If you have not already done so, you will want to find out how the governor feels about the bill to see if special lobbying is required to gain his or her support. If the bill is highly controversial, the industry will probably begin lobbying the governor's office and other key officials early in the legislative process. You should follow suit.

The above list seems endless, but more could be added. Add your own strategies and share them with members of your group who have not experienced this part of reform work.

Study your system well. You will probably learn one thing quickly — most individual legislators have meager resources to perform their duties. In most states there is no money for staff assistance except for legislators with important positions or those who chair large committees. Many legislators share secretaries. They are usually at the capitol only during the legislative session. Even then they must continue to tend to their own personal and business or professional affairs as well as the legislature. If they are conscientious (or ambitious), they will be extremely busy and overworked. They will be dealing with many issues other than nursing homes. Some will have priority because they are the legislator's pet issues or because (s)he is being pressured by time factors or because other lobbyists have been effective.

Be sensitive to the realities of the system and learn how you can fit in most effectively. You may be surprised to learn that if anything is to be done by an individual legislator, you and your group will have to provide actual labor to get it done. This means you may get involved in drafting bills. You will probably be needed to do "staff" work such as research and providing factual reports. Or you may have to tell the legislator what information (s)he needs to request from various government agencies. You will probably have to write a summary of the bill. You may be needed to run errands to pick up and deliver materials. You may end up helping to arrange special meetings for the legislator with various groups, or you may be drafting his/her speeches in support of the bill. Needless to say, you will not perform any of these services for any legislator not totally committed to fighting for the bill's passage. But in most states this is the "nitty-gritty" of the system which helps assure that your bill gets more attention than any of hundreds of other bills.

Lobbying for Administrative Reform

Administrative reform is crucial in most states. For example, the licensure agency may be dragging its feet in writing regulations to apply to new nursing home laws, or the old regulations may be weak and outdated. You may spot an existing law which, with specific regulations, could apply to nursing home residents; this occurred in Massachusetts with a consumer protection bill. You may want to lobby to see that consumer groups are represented in every meeting the regulatory agencies have with the industry as Citizens for the Improvement of Nursing Homes did in Seattle.

Some of the basic principles for legislative lobbying may

apply, but in this case you will be dealing directly with the bureaucracy. This can be just as discouraging and just as challenging. At times you will wonder who government agency people work for — the people or the nursing home industry.

There are several things to consider when lobbying administrative agencies:

1. Public employees are hired to serve the public so they should respond to your requests and recommendations or be held accountable for not doing so.

2. Public agencies such as the health and welfare departments usually have the power to issue regulations without having to go through the legislative process.

3. Public hearings regarding regulatory changes may or may not be required. You should press for them in any event, for it offers you an opportunity to get the facts before the public.

4. Most high administration officials (particularly the "appointed" ones) will bend to the will of elected representatives who intervene to fight any change or reform, particularly if pressured by the industry.

5. Most government agency employees have not had to deal directly with citizen groups, but they (like legislators) have probably met with industry representatives quite often at luncheons and dinners, special business meetings, conventions, educational workshops, and even golf on Saturdays.

Most inexperienced citizens are shocked to learn that public officials and employees may not be sympathetic or supportive of reform work which seems so "right and just" for people. Many employees will be, but others may feel personally threatened when they hear criticism of the system because they are friendly with providers or they are so entrenched in the system they can't see that it doesn't serve the people. It won't be easy for you to maneuver and keep your sense of humor in the administrative maze of most public agencies, but you can do it.

part 2: doing what needs to be done

5

REFORMING EXISTING LAWS AND
REGULATIONS

Given what a few citizens have done, we can be optimistic
about what many, many more like them can do in the near
future. The program and action ideas described in this section
by no means exhaust the possibilities open to creative and
responsible citizen activists. There is no prefab program or set
of infallible prescriptions for resolving all the problems in the
long-term care system. What follows is a sample of advocacy
and reform measures. Where there is no "answer" to specific
problems, we offer suggestions and approaches, or an account
of how a group tackled a certain problem. Project ideas should
be adapted to your own situation, your own community need,
and to resources available to you. Each project or action idea
should be viewed not as an end in itself, but as a bridge for
initiating other reform measures, each promoting consumer
protection and long-term care reform.

If the plight of nursing home residents is to be improved,
states must adopt higher standards than those presently established by federal legislation and regulations. When this happens, federal law requires compliance with the higher state
standards.

Although there is no single model state law to follow, several states noted below have taken recent action to improve
their laws. We suggest you order copies of laws and regulations
from states cited to use as models when working for legislative
or regulatory changes.

Citation System

A citation system enables prompt and effective civil sanctions to be taken against facilities in violation of state regulations. Minnesota has implemented a system giving the state the authority to fine a facility $250 for each deficiency not corrected within fifteen days of the correction order. California legislation empowers the department of health to levy fines with the amount to be increased for each day of continuing violation. There are two classes of violations with the fine related to the severity of the violation.

The New York Public Health Commissioner was given the power to impose fines of up to $1000 per day for any violations of applicable state laws, rules and regulations. Further, a system was established by which the Medicaid reimbursement rate would be reduced in sufficient amount to collect penalties.

In Iowa citations are classified according to the severity of the violation. A Class I violation presents an imminent danger or a substantial probability of resultant death or physical harm to facility residents. The licensee shall be subject to a civil penalty of not less than $500 nor more than $5000 for each violation. For Class II violations which relate to residents' rights, a licensee shall be subject to a civil penalty of not less than $100 nor more than $500.

Because the citation system was recently enacted, it is too soon to determine its effectiveness. If a facility is fined for each and every violation, it should serve as a deterrent — at least in those states where penalties are sufficiently high to affect profits. It is clear that other sanctions are needed to supplement the penalty of fines.

The California citation process may be initiated by anybody, and the name of the person bringing the complaint can remain anonymous. The complainant or his/her representative may accompany the inspector when (s)he inspects the facility with alleged violations. Each citation must be posted in plain view of patients, persons visiting patients, and those who inquire about placement in the facility. The department of health is required to publish and make available to the public an annual report listing all nursing homes and the status of any citation issued.

Unannounced Inspections

Nursing home operators claim it is not possible to conduct a "fair" inspection without their presence to provide records, answer questions, etc. While it is clear that inspectors will need to talk with the administrator if there are areas of serious non-compliance, it is equally clear that there should always be someone in the facility during regular daytime work hours who has access to records needed in a routine inspection.

Obvious cover-up maneuvers are possible and commonly used by nursing home operators who need to clean up their facilities and records for inspection purposes. Common sense motivates citizen groups and responsible government agencies to support the movement for unannounced inspections. Wisconsin, New York, California, Iowa, Rhode Island, and Minnesota have passed laws containing this provision.

Nursing Home Ombudsman

A few states have enacted legislation creating an office of nursing home ombudsman. In South Carolina, the nursing home ombudsman may investigate complaints and "may" issue a report and recommendations. All departments, officers, agencies, and employees of the state must cooperate with the ombudsman in carrying out the duties of the office. The original bill gave the office subpoena powers. This provision was deleted because of opposition from the South Carolina Nursing Home Association.

In 1975 the Maine Committee on Aging was authorized by law to serve as an advocate and ombudsman for residents. The committee has been given the power to enter any licensed facility to investigate complaints. It may authorize up to twenty-five persons, including committee members, staff of the committee, and other citizens, to carry out this function.

There are legislative proposals which would provide the clout necessary for an ombudsman to operate more effectively. One proposal in California would authorize the ombudsman to initiate civil litigation on behalf of residents. All complaints in the state would be directed to that office. Health care facilities would be required to provide the telephone number and address of the nearest ombudsman office. The bill would make it a misdemeanor for any long-term health care facility to retaliate against persons for communicating with the ombudsman office.

Residents' Rights Regulations

Federal residents' rights regulations are being used as a model for state legislation. Some of these laws are little more than platitudes because they have no real enforcement power and their provisions are general and vague. The basic premise of the regulations is good, but to be effective the language must be clarified, additional rights included, and mechanisms established which will assure they can be implemented and enforced.

In July 1975 an exceptional state law became effective in Colorado. Its nursing home rights bill requires that nursing homes establish a residents' advisory council and a specific grievance and complaint procedure. The council members are to be selected by the resident population and the council must meet at least once a month with the administrator and other staff to make recommendations regarding policies of the facility. The requirement for an advisory council, though excellent, provides that it be made up entirely of residents. It would be strengthened if the council had representation from outside the facility, although the majority should be residents. Outside members can add to the progress and implementation of the program. For example, they can serve as a link to community agencies and organizations that have some authority over nursing homes or provide services, including referrals of potential residents. They can keep residents apprised of community activities in which they can become involved.

The council may present grievances to the grievance committee on behalf of a resident. Special provisions related to the grievance procedure include: (1) each facility shall designate one full-time staff member to receive all grievances when they are first made; (2) each facility shall establish a grievance committee consisting of the chief administrator of the facility or his designee, a resident selected by the resident population, and a third person to be agreed upon by the administrator and the resident representative.

Patient Advocates

A 1975 Connecticut omnibus nursing home bill calls for the establishment of a patient advocate system. Although the law needs strengthening and effective regulations must be promulgated, it paves the way for development of an outstanding model for other states to follow.

The law provides that every local health director, board of health, or other local administrative body under the state health care system shall appoint a patients' advocate "if available." It is apparent that the "if available" provides a loophole for departments that don't want to become involved. Consumer groups are trying to amend the law by removing this phrase.

The patient advocate is someone who has demonstrated an interest in the elderly or has special background in geriatric care. Service is for two years without compensation. The advocate's responsibility is to report violations to the official agency. In addition, (s)he will (1) assure that the bill of rights is properly posted and distributed in each facility, (2) assure that all mandated posting of inspection reports is complied with, (3) aid patients in transfers and discharge procedures, and (4) receive and follow up complaints directed to the health department.

The state's nursing home ombudsman and private advocacy groups are organizing training programs for patient advocates. Selection criteria, training curricula, and job descriptions will have to be developed.

In Maryland an effort is underway to promote the development of an Office of Patient Advocate to enforce the bill of rights passed in 1975. This proposal promotes the idea that the office should be independent of both the nursing home industry and the state department of health. It proposes a public, nonprofit corporation similar to the public defender. An alternative approach would be to create and finance a separate division within Legal Aid. The patient advocate is seen as representing only the interests of the client, offering consultative services to residents about their grievances, and presenting these grievances to appropriate persons, offices, agencies, and courts. The proposal, developed by John J. Regan, is available from the National Council of Senior Citizens, Legal Research and Services for the Elderly, listed in the Resources section under "Other Special Resources."

Guaranteed Access to Nursing Homes

Denial of access to nursing homes prevents many visitors from acting vigorously to assist patients and will seriously impede the activities and success of ombudsmen and patient advocates. Chapter 3 discussed two approaches in which access rights can be protected: through litigation to enforce the constitutional rights of speech and association; and through enforcement of the patient-rights provisions in the Medicare/Medicaid regulations for SNFs and ICFs.

A third approach is through the enactment of state access legislation or regulations. Pennsylvania has issued specific access regulations and the Washington, D.C., City Council passed an ordinance which can serve as a model for other states and cities. The relevant section of the Pennsylvania regulations, Title 55, Section I, 325. *Access Requirements*, reads:

325.3 The facility shall permit members of recognized organizations and representatives of community legal service programs whose purpose includes rendering assistance without charge to patients to have access to the facility.

325.5 The purpose of these visits may be to:
  (a) Visit, talk with and make personal, social and legal services available to all patients.
  (b) Inform patients of their rights and entitlements and their corresponding obligations, under Federal and State laws, by means of educational materials and discussions in groups and with individual patients.
  (c) Assist patients in asserting their legal rights regarding claims for public assistance, medical assistance and Social Security benefits, as well as in all other matters in which patients are aggrieved. Assistance may be provided individually as well as on a group basis, and may include organizational activity as well as counseling and litigation.
  (d) Engage in all other methods of asserting, advising and representing patients so as to extend to them full enjoyment of their rights.

The District of Columbia, title III, section 3 of regulation number 74-15, uses similar language to express the purposes of visits, but one important provision is added. The purpose may also to be "(a)(4) Inspect all areas of the health care facility except the living areas of a patient who protests such inspections. Such authority shall not include the right to examine the business records of the facility without the consent of the Administrator, nor the clinical record of a patient without his consent.''

The best feature of the Washington, D.C., access ordinance is that it includes specific penalties for violation by a nursing home. Inclusion of provisions detailing specific penalties is critical to the effectiveness of access legislation. The provision is as follows:

Section 1. Penalties and Remedies

(a) Any person who violates any provision of this regulation shall be guilty of a misdemeanor and upon conviction shall be subject to a fine not to exceed $300.00, or to a term of imprisonment not to exceed ninety days.

(b) The imposition of any fine or term of imprisonment pursuant to subsection (a) of this section shall be in addition to any denial, suspension, revocation, or refusal to renew a health care facility license which may result from the violation.

(c) Each day of any violation shall constitute a separate offense, and the penalties prescribed above shall be applicable to each such separate offense, except that no further penalties shall be imposed for the period during which any appeal from a conviction of such offense is pending.

(d) Any person or representative thereof, who is damaged due to a violation of this regulation shall:

    (1) have a civil cause of action against any person violating this regulation, and

    (2) be entitled to recover from any such person:

        (A) Actual damages

        (B) Punitive damages

        (C) A reasonable attorney's fee and litigation costs reasonably incurred.

Guaranteed Access to Information

If your state does not have an effective code guaranteeing disclosure of documents and reports in possession of state agencies and departments, or if there are regulatory restrictions against disclosure, actions should be taken to change the laws or the regulations.

Model state freedom of information statutes can be obtained from the Freedom of Information Clearinghouse. The clearinghouse is a project of Ralph Nader's Center for Study of Responsive Law, which provides advice and legal assistance to groups and individuals striving to obtain access to information. Requests should be addressed to the clearinghouse at: P.O. Box 19367, Washington, D.C. 20036.

Recommend and work toward legislation and regulations guaranteeing public disclosure of *all* information submitted by nursing homes to governmental agencies and *all* information prepared by governmental agencies about nursing homes. Nursing home information received by government agencies from other sources, such as consumer complaint letters, should also be a matter of public record. The only limitation on public disclosure should be on information revealing the names of individual residents. Unless release is authorized by the resident or the resident's representative, the name should be removed from the information rather than using the name as cause for denying access to the entire document.

Many citizen groups have succeeded in obtaining disclosure of nursing home inspection reports. Citizens for Better Care in Detroit successfully initiated legal action for access to inspection reports. A group should not compromise by accepting disclosure of only a "summary"; the entire report should be available. In addition to inspection reports, all cost reports covering nursing home stock and any firms conducting business with nursing homes should be public information.

Access to information means nothing unless the public is aware that such information is available and knows how it can be obtained. A citizen group can inform the community of its right to information and methods for obtaining it. A group can demand that government agencies make concerted efforts to inform the public of its right to information, what types of information are available, and the means for obtaining such information. For example, demand that notices be posted in local Social Security and welfare offices indicating that Medicare/Medicaid inspection reports are available for public review.

Information must be readily accessible if individual consumers, potential consumers, professionals, and placement agencies are to determine which nursing homes are in compliance with rules and regulations and which are not. While trying to obtain information to select a facility, not everyone can travel to state offices to review inspection reports, nor should they have to. Citizen groups can work toward a requirement that all facilities post in a conspicuous place their current license status as well as a list of substantiated violations.

California legislation, Assembly Bill 1600, addresses this issue. A copy of a citation for a violation must be prominently posted, as we have noted, in a place or places in plain view of patients, persons visiting patients, and persons who inquire about placement in the facility. The licensee is further required to post a prominent notice informing such persons that copies of all final uncorrected violations issued by the department to the facility will be made promptly available by the licensee for inspection by any person who so requests it.

State Rules and Regulations

State laws are often written in general language and are difficult to interpret. Most state laws require that rules and regulations be promulgated by the agency administering the law. They can be adapted or changed without going through the legislative process. The public can offer suggestions for regulations or make recommendations for changes in regulations proposed by the agency. If you are working for strong regulations and find that your recommendations are being ignored or that the industry has too much influence, ask for public hearings before regulations are set. Since regulations usually state the intent of the law in great detail, they are as important as the law itself.

In February 1976 a comprehensive set of regulations for residents' rights became effective in Massachusetts. These regulations are unique, having been promulgated under the state Consumer Protection Act. The state attorney general has responsibility for implementation and enforcement of the Consumer Protection Act. The regulations define unfair or deceptive acts or practices, and they were designed to ". . . promote the comfort, health and well-being of consumers of services provided by nursing homes and to fill a void in existing regulations." Under this act the attorney general's office has the authority to investigate complaints relating to regulations covering charges for services, access to persons outside the facility, personal care, medical care, and discharge and transfers. The attorney general can taken action by imposing a fine for violations.

Other Innovative Legislation

In August, 1975, New York Governor Hugh Carey signed

thirteen bills designed to help solve some of the problems in his state's nursing homes.

The amendments to existing law include:

1. The establishment of liability of every person who is in a position of control. A controlling person is defined as "any person who has the ability, directly or indirectly, to direct or cause the direction of the management or policies of said facility."

2. The requirement that financial statements and information required by law or regulation be certified by an independent certified accountant who cannot have any financial interest in the facility. Any person intentionally or knowingly certifying a false financial statement or information shall be guilty of a felony.

3. The mandatory review of the character, competence, and standing in the community of proposed incorporators, directors, sponsors, stockholders, and operators. It must be substantiated that a consistent high level of care is being or was being rendered in each facility with which such person is or was affiliated.

Legislative reform in Iowa resulted from the work of Senator William Gluba and the Ralph Nader-initiated Iowa Student Public Interest Research Group. Some of the legislative amendments include:

1. Upon request of either a complainant or the department, a complainant or his representative or both may be allowed the privilege of accompanying the inspector during any on-site inspection based on the complaint.

2. Besides the authorized health department inspection, an inspector of the department of social services shall have inspection rights with respect to any facility where one or more of the residents are cared for entirely or partially at public expense.

3. Each health care facility shall have a care review committee whose members shall be appointed by the area-wide health planning council. The committee shall periodically review the needs of each resident.

In several states the direct involvement of the state attorney general's office and offices of the district attorneys in enforcement has led to improvements in the system as well as direct legal action against facilities. If your state regulatory agency is not doing an adequate job, approach these offices for investigation and action. Use California and the work of the Santa Clara Valley Coalition, described in Part Three, as a model.

6

REFORMING THE INSPECTION SYSTEM

To be certified and therefore eligible for Medicare and Medicaid reimbursement, the facility must be inspected. The inspection measures or evaluates the capacity of the facility to meet the standards required by law.

The training and qualifications of inspectors have been almost universally challenged as a result of consumer evaluations of facilities. Their demands for offical re-evaluation surveys have determined that facilities were not meeting the standards when inspection records indicated they were. The nursing home task force of the Santa Clara Valley Coalition's study of quality and consistency of inspection led to a formal questioning of the competence, qualifications, and attitudes of department of health personnel. They asked the state health director for a complete re-evaluation of the state's inspection system, including a review of job descriptions, qualifications, and a determination of each employee's commitment to changing the nursing home industry.

Inspection procedures should be reformed. They can best be conducted by well-trained teams including a nurse, social worker, safety engineer, dietician, administration specialist, and consumer representative. Unannounced inspections should be mandatory. The inspection should be for the official purpose "to inspect." Consultation to help the facility improve should *follow* the actual inspection.

The licensure agency in California is experimenting with using photographs to document health and safety violations. The state attorney general's office initiated a program for training investigative teams to use cameras to photograph evidence of violations where possible.

The same inspector should not inspect the same facilities year after year. A pattern of special friendships and loyalty to the facilities' personnel can develop, which interferes with objectivity and full reporting of deficiencies.

At the federal level, Senator Moss's 1975 legislative packet included a bill to require state inspections at least every ninety days. Another bill would require minimum qualifications for surveyors and another would create a cadre of federal inspectors to conduct spot checks of Medicare and Medicaid facilities to test the quality of state inspection procedures.

In order to assure continued quality control in Pennsylvania, the state ombudsman project recommended that a training officer be hired by the licensure agency to set up uniform training for new surveyors, to conduct periodic in-service education for all surveying staff, and to insure that new regulations and interpretations of regulations be conveyed to all surveyors.

The nursing home inspector's role is vital. We depend on this person to conduct a thorough, objective, and honest evaluation of conditions in the facility and its operation. To do the job well, the inspector must be highly qualified. Most inspectors of Medicare and Medicaid facilities have participated in special university-based training courses developed by HEW. Since the initiative for this training began in 1971, most of the two thousand people trained received instruction prior to the promulgation of new regulations in 1974. There has been no uniform training of inspectors regarding important regulations such as patients' rights, medical direction, and discharge planning.

Conduct a study to determine if all licensure and certification inspector-surveyors have received adequate training — particularly for the new federal regulations. Your study should include a review of each inspector's qualifications and a record of his/her training. If you find inadequacies, submit a report to the director of your state licensure agency and the director of the regional HEW Office of Long-Term Care (with a copy to the Long-Term Care Education Coordinator) outlining the need for special training. Request that your group be able to observe training so you can review quality and content. If thorough training regarding residents' rights is nonexistent or inadequate, ask to be included in the development of special training sessions for this purpose. Citizen group representatives can give valuable help in preparing such programs.

If you study the state licensure agency and find there are not enough inspectors to effectively evaluate nursing home conditions in regular and "spot" inspections, bring it to the attention of officials and elected representatives. If inadequate funds is the problem, mobilize support to have the legislature appropriate more money.

Fragmented inspection programs have been a glaring defect of the regulations in most states. A single state agency should be given full authority and responsibility for the licensure and certification process. It is unreasonable to assume quality control in inspection procedures when inspections are made by several different departments and inspection records, financial records, copies of complaints, etc., are in different state files.

Although one state agency should coordinate official inspections, every state employee who visits nursing homes for official reasons should be required to report any problems. Social workers with nursing home clients receiving state assistance should be responsible for reporting any conditions of neglect. Investigations and reports of state ombudsman programs should become part of the official record of the nursing home. Short evaluation forms, similar to those for many restaurants, could be prepared by the state licensure agency and made available in all nursing homes. In Maine, postcard forms pre-addressed to the state agency were prepared for residents' and visitors' use. Local health and welfare department officials should have the authority to conduct special investigations and the power to issue citations and levy fines.

Consumer Representation on Inspection Teams

There is a growing realization on the part of government agencies that consumers dedicated to nursing home reform are knowledgeable about nursing home standards and inspection procedures and forms. There is no reason why concerned consumers should not be involved in the inspection process. We know of no law preventing consumers from participating.

In California the state director of health gave consumers from the Santa Clara Valley task force on nursing homes permission to attend inspections when complaints were being investigated by health department officials, although they were not part of the inspection process.

An innovative model which included consumers in one part of the inspection process was adopted in the 1974 revised rules and regulations for health care facilities in Iowa: The regulations established a "care review committee" with the following duties:

"Each health care facility shall have a care review committee whose members shall be appointed by the areawide health planning council recognized as such by this state acting through the office for comprehensive health planning in the office for planning and programming. The care review committee shall periodically review the needs of each individual patient or resident of the facility . . . " The responsibilities of the care review committee were to be established in accordance with rules of the health department.

Representatives from different consumer and voluntary organizations can be trained to help conduct inspections dealing with residents' rights. Approach the health department with a written proposal for training citizen representatives for this task.

ENFORCING LAWS AND REGULATIONS

Generally state laws give an administering agency the authority to enforce the law and its regulations. This authority usually includes the power to revoke or suspend a license and to recommend that Medicaid or Medicare "provider agreements" be limited or revoked. These actions are rarely taken, even when facilities have significant deficiencies listed in inspection reports year after year.

Ask your state attorney general to give you an exact determination of enforcement powers in the law and what action the regulatory agency can take to enforce compliance. You may find that action to amend the law to establish a citation system is necessary to supplement existing enforcement provisions. Other actions to improve enforcement efforts include:

(1) Revising the language of standards and regulations. They are often vague and general; they should be explicit, measurable, and enforceable.

(2) Rating facilities according to the quality of care given. Deficiencies should be defined and graded; in 1975 the New York State Health Commissioner was authorized by law to develop a rating system based on public inspection deficiencies.

(3) Authorizing state agencies which place people in nursing homes to guide the placement of residents to facilities according to their deficiency records or rating. Since nursing homes often depend on these referrals to fill their beds, this procedure should serve as an incentive to correct deficiencies and maintain standards.

(4) Speeding up administrative hearing procedures. Nursing homes have the right to appeal action by the regulatory agency;

the hearing process can take several months or years. When necessary, regulations should be amended to permit residents, relatives, and community groups to testify at hearings where license and certification denials are being considered.

(5) Temporarily suspending or limiting a facility's operating certificate if conditions pose an imminent danger to the health or safety of any patient. In New York the commissioner has the power to do this and to limit the placement of new patients, remove existing patients, and to suspend or limit the payment of government funds.

(6) Developing new responses to the argument "We can't close this facility — there would be no place to put the patients." Unless we adhere to the ignorant assumption "a bad home is better than no home at all," this argument should never be accepted. Homes have been closed because the conditions were so bad that the residents' health and safety were actually harmed and there has always been another facility to accept the residents. Sometimes when serious conditions exist, the facility and its programs can be upgraded.

Under these circumstances, the state is faced with a dilemma: How do we protect the patient from poor care and unsafe conditions and how do we save them the trauma and pain associated with the process of relocation? No state has come up with an effective solution to this problem. Two proposals have been made which have merit. They are based on the premise that the state is responsible to protect individuals from the loss of their basic right to adequate health care.

Ben Abramovice, director of the Home for Jewish Parents in Oakland, California, has proposed that a facility be placed in a type of receivership he labels "protective custodianship." His plan calls for a court-appointed administrator to bring a substandard institution up to acceptable standards. After a two-year investigation of New York's nursing homes, state assemblyman Andrew Stein recommended a plan to make a community group or agency the "temporary trustee" of a substandard facility when care or conditions endangered patients. These proposals can be developed into a workable plan to propose in your state.

(7) Incorporating consumer group views in peer review systems. The American Health Care Association is promoting the development and implementation of peer review by all affiliated state associations. Many industry leaders contend that a

peer review system can strongly influence an administrator to maintain high standards. The Minnesota Association of Health Care Facilities received a $10,000 HEW grant in 1971 to establish a model peer review program. In the fall of 1975 ten state associations had adopted this system. The general plan has some merit in that it would supplement the official inspection process. But this model contains some undesirable provisions: homes are only surveyed every two years; the administrator is advised in advance of the survey and sent a survey form so that "he will be able to identify weak areas in his facility before the survey and begin at once to make corrections"; and if a serious complaint of negligence or abuse is received, a telephone call will be made to the administrator to inform him that a team will be sent to investigate. (If the home doesn't correct the problem within a certain period, a motion *may* be made to suspend or terminate the home's membership in the association.)

If the state nursing home association is promoting peer review in your state, evaluate the plan. Support strong provisions and denounce any weak ones, such as those above. Recommend that registered complaints from consumer groups, reports from any residents' councils, and interviews with residents and staff be included in the peer review process.

(8) Using litigation to compel government agencies at all levels to strictly enforce nursing home standards. *The Nursing Home Law Handbook*, prepared by Sally Hart Wilson for the National Senior Citizens Law Center, suggests several other possible legal actions. One is based on traditional tort and contract theories and brought by patients either as individuals or as class litigants. In New York nursing home patients may file a class action suit for damages or other relief for deprivations or infringements of their rights to adequate and proper treatment. Another kind of suit alleges unfair business practices and requests injunctive relief against the same. This is possible under the laws and regulations in Massachusetts.

(9) Using federal patients' rights regulations to promote compliance. According to Sally Hart Wilson, advocates for nursing home patients can argue that the following enforcement procedures are implicit in these regulations:

• *Decertification of Facility.* The protection of patients' rights is a condition of a facility's participation in the Medicare and Medicaid programs. The denial of such rights is ground for decertification to participate. Demand for decertification should be made to HEW officials at the regional and federal level.

• *Private Litigation.* The regulations may be used in private litigation cases on behalf of the patients whom they are designed to protect. Remedies might include both monetary damages, including punitives, and injunctive relief.

• *Fair Hearing.* With respect to Medicaid beneficiaries, a patient whose rights are being violated, should be entitled to a fair hearing at which he/she can demand either that the institution be ordered to extend him/her the rights guaranteed by law, or that he/she be transferred to a facility where such rights will be provided.

The National Senior Citizens Law Center will work with attorneys to invoke these enforcement mechanisms.

(10) Making the governing boards of nursing homes fulfill their obligations. Regulations require every nursing home have an identifiable authority which has full legal and moral responsibility for all aspects of facility operations. In most facilities this authority is called the "governing body," "board of directors," "board of trustees," or "owners." No matter what the formal name, this group has responsibilities and duties which cannot be delegated. Minimum standards outlined in the regulations require that the governing body must perform such duties as:

• Adoption of bylaws, patient care policies, administrative policies, and rules and regulations which govern and direct the operation of the facility;

• Appointment of a competent, licensed administrator with full responsibility for operating the nursing home in accordance with policies established by the board;

• Conducting meetings periodically, and for specific purposes, to take care of ongoing policy and operational matters of the nursing home. Minutes of the meetings must be kept as they are legal records of decisions made. Such decisions must be transmitted to those having direct operations responsibility; and,

• Providing assurance that the nursing home is operated in compliance with applicable federal, state, and local laws.

In the 1975 HEW national survey it was determined that "there is considerable evidence that the governing bodies of a large number of facilities do not properly carry out their duties and responsibilities in an effective manner, thus inhibiting the delivery of high quality care."

The nursing home administrator usually bears the brunt of all criticisms of the facility. Often the administrator is only carrying out the wishes of his/her board. The board usually remains nameless in the background when it should be just as visible and accountable as the administrator. Your group should identify each member of the governing body.

You may wish to make contact with a governing body primarily to recommend special actions benefiting residents such as forming a residents' council. Commend the board on any special features of the home indicative of quality care.

If the facility has noticeable problems you should write all members, reminding them of their responsibilities. Assure them that they will be held accountable to the public if they fail to take action. If conditions remain bad, you should bring their names to the attention of the public through the media or special reports. You may wish to ask for a special meeting of the governing body to directly present any complaints and recommendations for solving problems. If you still see no action, you may consider picketing these individuals' businesses or homes.

8

ENFORCING RESIDENTS' RIGHTS

A bill of rights with nice-sounding platitudes just isn't enough. Citizen groups must rally forces to propose and create special mechanisms assuring that residents' rights will actually be observed. Those discussed in this section relate to an individual's right to be involved in decisions affecting his/her life, and the right to actively seek improvement in his/her living conditions.

Grievance Committee

It seems necessary that one nursing home employee be authorized to receive complaints and coordinate any action to resolve them. The individual should be someone other than the administrator or staff involved in direct day-to-day patient care. Obviously in most nursing homes this leaves few choices. Someone responsible for social services could fill the role — ideally a trained social worker. It could also be a clergyman. Often the activities director is suggested, but it is clear that someone with a "recreation" orientation may not be even close to having the qualifications. Any person given this responsibility should have a thorough orientation in grievance procedures and residents' rights.

To be fair and effective, this person should never act alone. A grievance committee should be established to review each complaint and recommend solutions. The committee should be small (perhaps no more than seven persons) and the majority should be residents. Membership might also include a rep-

resentative of a local senior action group or a member of a
nursing home reform group, a member of a resident's family,
and a clergyman.

The staff person should clearly serve a supportive role on
the committee, and be involved in making decisions with the
committee, but not ever alone in behalf of the committee.
His/her responsibilities and the responsibilities of committee
members should be clearly outlined in writing for each resident and staff person.

Residents' Council

If organized effectively, a residents' council can be a special
means for residents to make their views known and become
involved in policy-making. It can also serve as a "court of appeal" if a resident is not satisfied with a grievance committee
decision.

One of the first public actions in promoting patients' rights
through an organized council occurred in Philadelphia in 1971.
The Welfare Rights Organization found that residents in the
Sarah Allen Nursing Home were being denied their rights.
They enlisted the Health Law Project of the University of
Pennsylvania to help organize a patients' rights committee.
Resistance from the nursing home had first barred organizers
from the facility. Legal action forced a settlement which gave
the organizers access to the nursing home, and eventually the
committee was established. Approximately 60 of the 150
patients attended the first meeting.

Although there have been isolated examples of nursing
homes with vital residents' councils or committees since the
early 1970s, only recently have they been seriously considered
as a possible requirement under federal and state standards.
With the present emphasis on residents' rights, even the industry is beginning to consider this avenue as one with great potential, at least as a public relations effort. At the 1975 annual
meeting of the National Council of Health Care Services, a special public relations task force urged the organization go on
record as encouraging its members to develop resident councils.
In the same meeting, the American Health Care Association
conducted an afternoon educational symposium on residents'
councils.

In a progressive paper on "Patients' Rights and Public Accountability," the New York Health Facilities Association concluded that "the creation of Residents' Advisory Councils is the most valuable mechanism for the assurance of continued maintenance of patients' rights and the achievement of a full measure of public accountability for the facilities which we represent."

Guidelines for *Establishing Resident Councils* were published in 1974 by the Division on Aging of the Federation of Protestant Welfare. This model proposes all members of the facility be members of the council. Elected officers and committees carry out the administration of the council. Unfortunately, these guidelines do not encourage outside representation.

One important function of any resident council should be official input in the licensure inspection process. The council's records should serve to indicate how the nursing home meets standards, particularly for patients' rights, on a day-to-day basis. Furthermore, inspectors should be authorized to interview several council members directly. Residents not actively participating in the council as officers or committee members should be interviewed to help evaluate the effectiveness of the council.

The perfect model for residents' councils has not yet been created, since it is a new concept in nursing homes. Consumer groups are urged to deliberate on this issue and offer a good model to their local nursing homes if none exists. Besides the above considerations, here are some other guidelines:

• A printed record of council activities should be on file and made available to residents. Council actions should be summarized and the summaries given to the residents soon after they are taken.

• Officers and committee members should be elected by the residents and their terms limited so all residents have an opportunity to become candidates.

• A staff person should be designated to serve as liaison between the administrator and the council. This liaison could be the same person who works with the grievance committee. In any event, the person coordinating the grievance committee should attend council meetings. The administrator should attend only at the council's invitation, but should always be apprised immediately of discussion or action at the meetings.

• A member of a resident's family could be a helpful council member.
• Meetings should be regularly scheduled, posted, and open to any residents.

It would be a major advance if a member of the residents' council were able to present the council's views and decisions directly to the board of the nursing home. The board should have the responsibility for reviewing the council's actions and recommendations.

HELPING THE CONSUMER: NURSING HOME
INFORMATION SERVICE AND DIRECTORY

Getting information to potential users of a service is always difficult. Although the various referral services, information centers, health care facilities, and public and private agencies publicize the services and programs available, most older people and their families are unaware of such sources. Data on long-term care resources, services, costs, and eligibility for and quality of care are often fragmentary and inadequate, or not available at all. The information needed to select a nursing home or to find an available alternative is difficult to get, and decisions are based on rumors and hearsay. Few products and services on the market today are more of a "blind item" than nursing home care. The average citizen has no idea what (s)he is buying.

Providing comprehensive consumer information is an essential, valuable activity for a citizen group.

Developing a Nursing Home Information Service

As will be described in Part Three, the nursing home information service organized by the Washington, D.C., chapter of the National Consumers League provides a centralized file of inspection reports on nursing homes participating in the Medicare/Medicaid reimbursement programs. The consumer can make convenient use of official government records as one means of selecting a nursing home.

Prepare a Consumer Handbook —
"How to Choose a Nursing Home"

The most frequent questions asked by citizens, professionals, and media representatives are "How do I choose a nursing home?" and "What *is* a good nursing home?" Although HEW, the nursing home associations, and some consumer groups have published handbooks, there continues to be a great need for wider dissemination and for better written materials.

Citizen groups can prepare a consumer handbook describing available options — alternative and home care services as well as nursing home care. The Medicare and Medicaid programs could be presented to explain the differences between skilled nursing care and intermediate care, and the eligibility requirements and benefits of each program. The handbook would detail how an older person, or family member, can begin the process of looking for a nursing home. It should first describe the kinds of care, services, and programs which are minimum requirements for all nursing homes; then describe the kinds of care, services, programs, attitudes, and type of environment generally found in better nursing homes.

The cost is a crucial issue, and the shopper must have a clear understanding to avoid problems. The handbook should discuss special fees above the basic rate, deposits, and lifetime contracts, to alert the shopper to key questions that must be answered before entering a nursing home.

A checklist of questions and observations for comparing facilities is a helpful tool. Citizens for Better Care and the University of Michigan/Wayne State Institute of Gerontology have prepared *How to Choose a Nursing Home: A Shopping and Rating Guide* that can serve as a model. See the Resources section for other consumer guides.

Prepare a Nursing Home Directory

Although most state licensure agencies publish an annual "directory" of nursing homes, they usually contain no information other than the name and address of the facility, the category or skill level, the number of beds, and the license number. Consumers and families need comprehensive, detailed information about specific institutions in their communities.

The facility name, a classified ad, an attractive outside appearance, fancy framed certificates, and phrases such as "approved
for Medicare" can be very misleading and tell the consumer
little if anything about quality of care. The travel and recreation industry have systems for rating restaurants and motels
across the country, but no one has devised a rating system for
nursing homes where a person might be spending the rest of
his/her life. An action group can provide an invaluable service
by preparing and distributing a nursing home directory rating
facilities qualitatively and containing essential, accurate information about each local home.

Your group can get information from three sources: a survey
sheet mailed to each facility, state/federal inspection reports,
and a visit and inspection of the facility, including interviews
with the administrator and/or staff members. A mailed survey
approach runs the risk of a low return rate, as Friends and
Relatives of Nursing Home Patients experienced. And the
validity of the information is questionable. The consumer
must have confidence that information provided is truthful.

The Medicare/Medicaid inspection reports are a valuable
source, but, as we have pointed out earlier, not all facilities in
a given community are certified for either program. Unless
state inspection reports are publicly disclosed, you will not
have information on all community facilities.

A research design and investigative tool must be carefully
planned and implemented if a group chooses to offer material
based on actual interviews and inspections. In 1975, the Urban
Institute (Washington, D.C.) received a grant from the Administration on Aging to design a form for consumers surveying
and evaluating nursing homes. The form will be offered with a
guide for effective volunteer use. The project results will need
careful review by experienced consumer groups.

Researching and preparing a directory for all nursing homes
in a state can be an awesome task — perhaps too large a venture for most groups. Groups have had a higher success rate
preparing directories for their own communities. Persuade a
state agency to prepare a statewide directory and rating system. If persuasion fails, demand it.

Data on nursing homes are constantly changing, so a group
will have to constantly update material. By the time a directory goes to press or the mimeograph machine, some facilities
may have closed, others opened, there will be changes in

licensing status, and no doubt the costs will have risen. Don't be discouraged or allow this to deter you from action. Remember that most consumers have no information. Whatever information you provide will certainly be more helpful than no information at all. Some samples from directories follow.

Over a five-year period, Bertha P. Peck and Tatiana L. Lowe, who served as volunteers with the Social Service Advisory Committee of the Northern Westchester Hospital, Mt. Kisco, New York, visited and evaluated area nursing homes and related care facilities. In 1970 their directory was published as a public service by the Mt. Kisco Chamber of Commerce. No attempt was made to rate the medical or nursing care. Yet, the directory is most informative and offers a personal reaction for each facility. The format used to describe the sixty facilities is illustrated below:

Name_____

Address_____

Phone_____

Owner_____   Administrator_____

Classification: SNF, Approved for Medicaid

Rates: $165 - $210 weekly   Number of patients: 71

Transportation: Bus service to White Plains or 40 minutes by car
   from Mt. Kisco. 5 blocks from railroad.

Special Features: Low rates. Wine or cocktails allowed with meals.
   Will take mildly disoriented.

Physical Plant: Small outmoded hospital in quiet residential section
   of Tarrytown. Big trees and attractive plantings, outdoor sitting
   areas. Some sub-standard structural features and crowded conditions, but very clean.

PERSONNEL: Administrator: British R.N. trained in England with
   administrative experience in U.S.A. Unusually capable and sympathetic; medically alert, treats patients with respect and consideration.

Staff: Young and neat.

PATIENTS: Most Medicaid; simple background. Many wheelchair
   and walker cases; few bedridden. Some disoriented and senile.
   Women preferred.

At the conclusion of its demonstration project, the Citizens Monitoring Team prepared a directory of the Davenport (Iowa) facilities it visited and inspected. Citizens using the directory were urged to look at the full reports prepared by CMT, available for public review in the mayor's office. The fire-safety and health licensing status was noted for each facility over a thirteen-month period to offer a historical as well as a current view of the licensing status. The following is a sample entry:

Name of Facility, Address, Owner, Administrator				
	2/1974	8/1974	12/1974	2/1975
Public Health Licensing Status	full	full	full	full
Fire Licensing Status	full	full	full	full

Strengths: New building is extremely well planned. Five meals a day program. Recreation room, activities director, and a good staff in-service training. Aides are unionized.

Weaknesses: Those residents designated as "senile" are placed in the older part of the building. The extra charges for hand-feeding and changing are comparatively high.

Sage Advocates Program in New Haven, Connecticut, is an associate organization of the Downtown Cooperative Ministry supported by funds from Protestant and Catholic groups and the New Haven Foundation. In 1976 Sage published a directory of "New Haven Area Nursing Homes: Summaries of 21 Medicare/Medicaid Inspection Reports." The one-hundred page document offers background information on the long-term care system, the Medicare/Medicaid programs, and the state inspection procedures. The directory includes information and guidelines for the selection of a nursing home.

The format is similar to the "digest" that will be described in Part Three that the National Consumers League devised. The listing begins with the name, address, phone number, patient census information, and the dates of the inspector's initial survey and the date of the revisit survey. Inspection results are listed in several categories: administration and personnel; Medicare service; dietetic services; pharmaceutical services; rehabilitation and other professional services; physical environment; fire safety; and any other deficiencies or comments documented by the inspector. The number and title of the deficient standard is listed, followed by the inspector's written observations and explanation. Results of the revisit

inspection are also given with a notation of whether improvements had been made. (Sage Advocates Program is located at
53 Wall Street, New Haven, Connecticut 06510.)

In 1973, Carol A. Delany, the Pennsylvania nursing home
ombudsman, released a consumers' handbook on nursing
homes which includes a directory of SNFs and ICFs in south-
eastern Pennsylvania. The information was obtained from the
state inspection records and a questionnaire submitted to all
nursing homes. Homes that did not reply were listed with an
"xxxx." Of the 193 facilities listed, 75 made no response to
the questionnaire. Listed are the name, address, phone number, number of beds, and the licensing status, whether or not
the facility accepts Medicaid patients, if it is approved for
Medicare, length of the waiting list, and the daily rate. Also
listed is whether or not the facility has an operating resident
council, any special services, programs, and professional staff.
The handbook includes information on how to select a facility,
patients' rights, and alternative long-term care.

Consumer Representation on Boards and Committees

Decisions regarding nursing homes are often made by special
state and community boards which do not have consumer
members. Many boards are totally out of touch with consumer
needs. Members are often more interested in pursuing their
own private interests or those of local politicians, businessmen,
or the medical profession than in serving the public.

Boards and committees required to have consumer representatives may include: state licensure boards, state nursing home
administrators' licensure boards, licensure boards for health
professionals — nurses, doctors, social workers, etc., state and
area commissions or councils on aging, and local and state
health planning agencies, including the new Health Systems
Agencies and the statewide health coordinating councils. The
federal government is in the process of establishing a quality
control system to monitor health care through the Professional
Standards Review Organization (PSROs). Boards are being set
up at the state and local levels. Local board membership is
presently restricted to practicing physicians. Consumer groups
are pressuring the federal PSRO agency to change this ruling to
include consumer representation.

Your group should be aware of members of boards and committees who might become advocates for nursing home residents. Upon inquiry, you may be advised that there is "consumer representation." If true, you should approach the person serving to determine if (s)he actually knows the problems and issues. It is fairly common for local businesspersons or professional organization "joiners" to be appointed to community boards. Unless you find that they do in fact represent nursing home residents, they will need a lot of help and education from your group. If their actions show that they do not represent the public interest despite your educational efforts, it may be necessary to call for their replacement. Often board members are in conflict of interest. A "consumer representative" might be a relative of someone who owns part of a local nursing home or a pharmacist with nursing home contracts. These conflicts should be reviewed, exposed, and if necessary, resignations should be demanded.

If consumer representation is not provided, press for reform. Meanwhile, present your suggested reforms or recommendations in writing to the committees and give each the opportunity to act on them. If the board remains unresponsive, use citizen pressure to make it responsive. Tell the story to the media, influential organizations and individuals, and elected representatives. Enlist the help of responsible government agencies. Hold public hearings or conduct consumer picketing to highlight the issue.

It is critical that consumer representatives be responsible and accountable to the public. When they lack essential information, they can easily be intimidated or co-opted by providers or professionals serving on the boards. If they are not knowledgeable about the issue when appointed, they must be educated and trained by groups like yours.

ACTION ON NURSING HOME
COMPLAINTS

Government mechanisms for receiving, investigating, and resolving nursing home complaints vary from state to state. Some have an extensive complaint procedure while others have virtually no established procedure. The new California legislation created an innovative complaint procedure whereby upon receipt of a written complaint, the state department of health must institute an inspection within ten working days. The individual complainant or others mentioned in the complaint may choose to remain anonymous. The department must promptly inform the complainant of the proposed course of action and the complainant has the right, as we've noted, to accompany the inspector to the site of alleged violations.

Once an action group has begun to organize and has generated publicity in the community, it can expect to receive phone calls and letters from people with complaints who don't know what to do or where best to complain.

Although your group may choose not to act as ombudsman and not to develop a volunteer nursing home action center as described elsewhere in this section, you cannot ignore these complaints and requests for information and assistance. At the very minimum, the group can act in a referral role, suggesting the most effective approach toward resolution of a complaint. It is very important that you build and maintain an accurate file on agencies handling complaints.

One of the early research activities for a newly organized citizen group is to determine the state's policy, procedures, and mechanisms for handling nursing home complaints. If you reside in Idaho, Massachusetts, Michigan, Pennsylvania, Oregon,

South Carolina, or Wisconsin, your state has a HEW-funded nursing home ombudsman program. They were originally funded as three-year demonstration projects and at least partial HEW funding is continuing through 1976. Complaints should be referred to their offices.

In 1975, state agencies on aging were issued special funds by the Administration on Aging to enable the agencies to employ state Ombudsman Development Specialists. As we've noted, the task of these specialists is to provide leadership to state and area agencies on aging and local community/citizen groups for developing and promoting volunteer ombudsman activities. Most states are currently developing these programs.

Some states are using the AoA funds to develop a complaint center. Rather than retain these special funds to develop their own ombudsman programs, some states have contracted with other agencies, such as community legal services. Contact your state or area agency on aging to determine whether or not a complaint program has been established in your state.

In most states, the most appropriate place for complaint referrals is the state agency responsible for licensing and inspecting nursing homes, either the health or welfare department. Contact the agency head and ask for a written description of the complaint procedure. You should request the following information: (1) name, title, address, and phone number of the individual and agency to whom complaints should be addressed; (2) whether telephone complaints will be accepted and acted upon; (3) whether anonymous complaints, either written or telephoned, will be accepted and acted upon; (4) whether a complainant can remain anonymous when the department is investigating the facility in question; (5) whether a specific department employee is responsible for handling complaints, and if so, the person's name; (6) what specific types of information should be included in a consumer complaint letter; (7) what action the department takes when it receives a complaint; (8) whether and *when* the complainant will be notified of any pending action or the results of any action; (9) whether the complainant can accompany the department investigator when inspecting the facility or when questioning the nursing home administrator or staff; and (10) whether all files, reports and any other written documentation or communications regarding the complaint will be available to the complainant for review.

After obtaining this information, outline it in a brief, specific form and make it available to your membership. The outline can be used as a guideline for providing consistently accurate information on how and where a citizen can file a complaint.

Although each state may have its own mechanism for handling complaints, there are general guidelines that any individual or group can incorporate into their plan of action. Any plan must depend on the type and severity of the complaint. If, for example, the complaint is based on something that is not an immediate threat to the health and safety of the residents, such as the lack of activity programs, a letter of complaint to the regulatory agency will be appropriate. If there is an immediate threat to health and safety, plan immediate intervention. If residents are being beaten, locked in closets, or denied food or water, that is alleged criminal action and the police department should be notified immediately as well as the head of the regulatory agency.

Guidelines for Making Complaints

Here are some general guidelines for attempting to resolve nursing home complaints:

(1) It is essential that the complainant always bring the complaint to the attention of the director of nursing and the administrator of the nursing home first. The complaint might be resolved at this stage. Ask what corrective action will be taken — why the problem or deficiency has not been corrected earlier. Ask for a specific date on which you can expect the problem to be corrected. Maintain a written record of whom you spoke to, what was said, and any promises of action from the administrator.

(2) After you have filed the complaint with the director of nursing and the administrator, bring the complaint to the attention of the regulatory agency responsible for licensing and inspecting nursing homes, or the nursing home ombudsman office. In most instances, a complaint should be in writing and signed. *A note of caution:* it is very important that complaints be made as objectively as possible. Make your points clear and detailed without exaggeration. Make sure that the facts are more than hearsay. Include names, dates, times, and any other

specifics relevant to the case. Say that you expect a reply on a certain date.

If you have suggestions about how the complaint or problem might be resolved, state them in your letter. If you think the complaint warrants an immediate investigation, demand it. Often the regulatory agency will notify the administrator of a pending complaint investigation. Ask that an *unannounced inspection* be made. If the problems occur at night, request that the inspection be made at night. Remember, regulatory agency personnel are public servants. Your tax dollars are paying their salaries to protect the health and welfare of nursing home residents.

(3) Keep a copy of the complaint letter for your file and send a carbon to the facility in question. Copies can also be sent to the local and/or state consumer protection agency, the state attorney general's office, your congressman, and the state nursing home association. If you know the owner of the facility, send a copy to that individual or corporation. If the particular facility is affiliated with a state or national chain, a denomination, or organization, send a copy to the state and/or national headquarters.

(4) The Secretary of HEW has designated the local Social Security office as a clearinghouse for consumer complaints against facilities participating in the Medicare reimbursement program and the local welfare office for facilities participating in Medicaid programs. Although these local offices are not responsible for investigating complaints, they are the official agencies to receive them. The district office forwards complaints to the appropriate regulatory agency and the regional HEW office. The effectiveness of this procedure, however, has been questioned. It would be best to send a copy of the complaint to these offices rather than begin the process there.

(5) Find out what deficiencies, problems, and/or abuses have been noted on previous inspection reports, how long the problems have existed, and what has been done to correct them. You might discover that the same complaint has been made previously, or noted during earlier inspections. With this knowledge, you might have a stronger case. If the problem has been allowed to continue too long, demand that it be corrected immediately.

(6) Remember that professional personnel in nursing homes, the registered nurses and the licensed practical/vocational

nurses, administrators, and in some states, social workers, are
licensed to practice by state licensure and regulatory boards.
In most states, licenses are subject to revocation if, upon investigation and hearing, the licensee is found guilty of mental or
professional incompetence, gross immorality or a felony, being
an alcoholic or drug addict, or guilty of unprofessional conduct. Complaints against individual RNs and LPNs should be
directed to the state board of nursing. The licensing body for
administrators is usually called the "State Board of Examiners
for Nursing Home Administrators." Complaints against individual physicians can be lodged with the state board of medical
examiners. Copies of complaints should be forwarded to the
state regulatory agency and the office of the state attorney
general. Most professional organizations contend that they
have established peer review programs, so send a copy of the
complaint letter to the state professional association.

(7) Substantial documentation of nursing home problems or
deficiencies can be compiled if you ask visitors to keep a written record of what they observe. For example, you might ask
them to record the number of employees they see on duty
each visit; the appearance of the home; whether residents look
well cared for; whether residents are visiting with others;
whether the nurses' call device is located so a resident can
reach it; the quality and quantity of food served; and any
other direct observations relating specifically to the complaint
or deficiency.

(8) Often nursing home personnel will be the complainants.
Their complaints may be directed at working conditions. Obviously, poor working conditions have considerable effect on
quality of care. Frequently personnel will have valid complaints
directly related to patient care, patient abuses, or unsafe structural conditions. Ask the staff person to maintain a written
record of what (s)he observes, the availability or lack of equipment and supplies, the procedure for medication administration, etc. A sensitive, angry employee can be a good ally.

(9) If there has been no action on the complaint — or unsat-
isfactory action — bring the complaint to the attention of
other appropriate individuals and groups who might be able to
exert pressure. These include:

  • The HEW regional office — Long-Term Care Standards
    Enforcement Division

- City officials — mayor, councilmen, city attorney
- County commissioners
- State and county board of health members
- State elected representatives
- Health and welfare associations
- Local ministerial alliances and/or individual churches
- State and area agencies on aging
- Senior citizen groups and centers
- Local and state medical societies
- Local and state professional associations

(10) If it appears difficult to influence action, and if the enforcement agency has failed to respond to your request or failed to force correction of a deficiency, you might begin applying strong, unified daily pressure on the nursing home, the administrator, the owner, and the regulatory agency. It will convince them that your concern is legitimate, that you have objective, documented evidence, that you won't give up until action is taken.

(11) Ask the cooperation of local religious, civic, and women's groups, etc. Urge friends and relatives of residents to visit the nursing home more frequently. Ask the cooperation of the local newspaper. Issue press releases stating the problem, actions you have taken, and the lack of regulatory response. This phase might call for the use of creative, mass-based tactics. You might plan to picket or demonstrate at the facility, at the private residence of the owner or administrator. A press conference might be held outside the door of the enforcement agency, calling attention to the lack of action. Use mailed "zaps" as a tactic. A zap is a form of symbolic shock therapy aimed against the status quo. A zap can be contradictory, it can be humorous in content but deadly serious in intent. For example, if the facility has generally poor conditions, like being infested with roaches or flies, mail a letter of complaint and a box of roaches or flies to the owner, and send a copy of the letter with a news release to the press and the regulatory agency.

Establish a Complaint Action Center

A citizen group can establish a volunteer center to receive, refer and/or act upon nursing home complaints. Let the public know that it will serve as a hotline, receiving complaints from residents, family and friends, staff, and other professionals related to nursing homes. The volunteer ombudsman can assist the complainant in one of two ways. The caller might only need to be referred to an appropriate legal, medical, regulatory, or other agency for assistance. Or, the caller might need direct assistance from the group filing and resolving a particular complaint. The volunteer would assist in preparing a formal letter of complaint, forward it to the appropriate agency, and then serve as a mediator and monitor. Often, regulatory agencies tend to ignore complaints from individuals. It is difficult for the agency to ignore a complaint if a citizen group of twenty people stands behind the individual complainant.

Other consumer-oriented services could be added to the complaint/action center's program. For example, in developing a nursing home hotline, the Denver Gray Panthers planned to provide in-depth personal counseling with potential residents and their families. A counselor would attempt to calm some of the anxiety and fears about nursing homes, help the family and potential resident examine alternatives to nursing home care and differences among nursing homes within the community. When appropriate, the counselor would attempt to involve the resident in the decision to move into a nursing home. The counseling would be available prior to entry, during the resident's stay, and when a resident was discharged or transferred to another facility.

IMPROVING THE STATUS AND COMPETENCE
OF NURSING HOME PERSONNEL

Nursing home work poses little attraction to professional and ancillary health care workers. The general public and health care workers usually view this work as uninteresting, depressing, and second rate. Quality and safe patient care are largely dependent on the competence of the staff. Yet most aides and orderlies, who provide eighty to ninety percent of patient care, have little formal education and most receive little or no training. Most aides are grossly overworked and underpaid, with no fringe benefits and little hope for advancement. To make it worse, aides receive no public recognition, support, or rewards for their services.

Your group might consider initiating or supporting the following:

1. Recommend and lobby for a mandatory state certification program for nurse aides and orderlies. Establish regulations requiring all facilities to hire only certified personnel as a condition for licensing. The certification process should require preservice education and training of ancillary workers, complete with a screening mechanism. The relative ease in obtaining employment as an aide has attracted drug addicts and those with criminal records because references and records are seldom checked. The certification program should also include the development and implementation of procedures for screening prospective employees.

2. Initiate and support the development of geriatric-aide training programs. The training curriculum should include the psychological, physiological, and sociological aspects of the aging process. Older community people can be used in con-

sciousness-raising programs, sensitizing aides to the effects of
aging. The Kansas City Gray Panthers have begun a geriatric-
aide program and the Santa Clara Valley Nursing home task
force is supporting a similar venture.

3. Begin actions to improve salaries and fringe benefits for
nurse aides and orderlies. Nursing home wages ought to be
competitive with other health care institutions. Offer nurse
aides support in organizing for improved working conditions,
higher salaries, and protection of rights. The 1974 provisions
of the Taft-Hartley Act should result in increased unioniza-
tion, collective bargaining, and other union activity in nursing homes. Workers are now protected by the National Labor
Relations Board. Tish Sommers, Chairperson of the National
Organization for Women's Task Force on Older Women and
Marion Ballentine of Spokane's Citizens for the Improvement
of Nursing Homes are supporting efforts to increase nurse aide
salaries and other benefits.

4. Find ways to give recognition to professional and ancillary workers. Meaningful community award programs ought
to be established. The Central Bureau for the Jewish Aged
recognizes paraprofessionals with the Libby Asofsky Humani-
tarian Award. Winners of the outstanding patient care award
receive a citation and $150.

Organize a one-day conference, workshop, convention, wine
and cheese party, etc., for nurse aides in your community. The
purpose of such a gathering could be to give recognition;
solicit their concerns about nursing home problems and their
recommendations for improvements; offer pertinent information about union organizing and new patient care programs;
and offer a forum for consciousness-raising, discussing attitudes about aging. Include local nurse aides in the conference
planning and implementation. Approach the local of District
1199, National Union of Hospital and Health Care Employees,
or any other union that has organized nurse aides or orderlies
in your communities.

5. Recommend regulations establishing minimum staffing
ratios for patients and staff and for supervisory staff and nursing personnel. Senator Moss has recommended staffing ratios
providing a minimum of 2.25 hours of nursing time per patient
per day. Connecticut's regulations require a minimum of one
registered nurse on the day shift for every 30 patients, one
on the afternoon shift for every 45 patients, and one for every

60 patients on the evening shift. HEW, as well as most state regulatory agencies has refused to promulgate nurse staffing ratios, contending that the ratio of patients to personnel is not indicative of quality of care nor the amount of care available and actually provided to patients. Consumer groups and the Senate Subcommittee on Long-Term Care have argued that ratios are simply one way to ensure an increase in RNs and LPNs required in nursing homes. With no minimum ratio, the number of licensed personnel will remain inadequate and unlicensed aides and orderlies will continue to provide eighty to ninety percent of care.

6. Encourage accountability sessions and action programs to spur local and state nurses' assocations and colleges of nursing to develop and require curricula in geriatrics and gerontology. The state boards of nursing set legal requirements and approve curricula for schools of nursing. Most states continue to require curricula and clinical experiences in maternal and child health, even though the birth rate has dropped and the number of living old people has increased so significantly. Encourage schools of nursing to move the educational orientation and introduction to nursing from the acute-care hospital to the long-term care setting. Ask the nursing home industry to open its doors to educational institutions which will need clinical sites for nursing students.

SUPPORTING INNOVATION

In most communities there are good nursing homes with innovative patient care programs. In every state professionals are engaged in pioneering, innovative work to improve their roles as providers and to improve quality of care. Innovative roles and programs must become the rule, however, rather than isolated examples. Citizen groups must identify those facilities offering safe, high-quality care and give recognition and support to staff who are concerned and committed to improving the residents' quality of life. Citizen groups can work with other community facilities and professional groups to start similar programs.

During the twenty-two hearings from 1969 to 1973, the Senate Subcommittee on Long-Term Care conducted a careful search for those positive, innovative programs that distinguish the nation's finest nursing homes. The results are documented in the supporting paper number 6, "What Can Be Done in Nursing Homes: Positive Aspects in Long-Term Care."

The subcommittee learned that a good nursing home has many variables, but there are two important factors: (1) a firm belief that the elderly's physical and mental problems are, to a substantial degree, preventable; that even when these problems are present they are, more often than not, reversible, and (2) a belief in basic human dignity — helping patients to help themselves.

The subcommittee identified four major categories of innovation in nursing home care. The first is the positive approach to therapy and rehabilitation. A variety of techniques are used to enhance the mental and physical functioning of patients.

They include: (1) *reality orientation* to put a mentally re-
gressed patient into renewed contact with the world around
him; (2) *sensory training*, a therapeutic program designed to
reduce sensory deprivation; and (3) *remotivation*, essentially
an effort to find out what activities a patient enjoyed earlier
in life, or ones (s)he would have enjoyed, and direct him/her
toward those same goals.

The second category is improvements in the physical structure of nursing homes leading to better patient care and greater comfort. Innovations include "campuses" for older people
with the broad range of health care services in one location,
and a use of color and design that makes nursing homes more
appealing.

Positive, innovative approaches to educating and utilizing
employees is the third category. Probably the most interesting
program is employee sensitivity training, requiring prospective
employees to assume a patient's role for twenty-four hours before employment and, once hired, at regular intervals. Several
nursing homes have developed a "Patient for a Day" program
where staff members are periodically given a "diagnosis," a
patient gown, and a bed. The employee spends the workday
experiencing the frustration, anxiety, and needs as if (s)he
were a patient with that particular diagnosis. Many nursing
homes have begun an accident prevention program and in-
service and continuing-education programs. Many nursing
home associations have developed excellent educational multi-
media materials.

The fourth major area of innovation involves patient care
activities and services. Comprehensive activity programs are re-
placing the television and once-a-week bingo games. Self-
government is increasing with the establishment of resident
councils. Good nursing homes not only find ways to bring the
community into the nursing home, they also find ways to take
the nursing home out to the community.

Some state nursing home associations have developed peer
review programs, and have adopted a code of ethics encouraging good care and disciplining those members found continually in violation. The Illinois Association of Health Care Facilities has a statewide "cool line" whereby patients and their
families can call a toll-free number to register complaints
about any facility.

part 3: citizens' action nationwide

CITIZEN ACTION GROUPS

In the past few years a number of courageous and vigilant citizen groups have organized to campaign for long-term care reform. The actions of some of these groups are reported in this section. The summaries offer only a reflection of why an and how the groups were formed and what their main thrusts have been. The last seven serve as more comprehensive examples of either an effectively organized group or how a particular reform program was developed and implemented

You might contact groups directly to learn about their programs and strategies. Most operate on a shoestring budget and expenses are paid out of the pockets of volunteers. You might offer donations to cover cost and postage of any materials you request.

The resources these groups have in common are responsible citizens who have the commitment, courage, and drive to work successfully in the public interest. They persevere because they have seen the suffering of other citizens who are isolated from the resources of the community and do not have the strength to improve their living environment alone.

In this space we are only able to refer directly to leaders and organizers, but we fully realize that every member of each group deserves public recognition and support. Many are new to public-interest work. They are learning as they go, and many are becoming experts in the process. They are highly spirited and concerned and their work serves as a stimulus and model for all of us to follow.

New York Gray Panther Nursing Home Action Group
Contact: Ms. Ann Wyatt
424 East 62nd Street
New York, New York 10021   (212) 755-0876

The New York Gray Panther Nursing Home Action Group
was formed in November 1974 at a general Gray Panther organizing conference. Since that time, the group has concentrated on patients' rights.

In April 1975 the group officially launched "Project Remember" in response to the closing of nursing homes with un-
correctable fire hazards in New York City. They recruited and
trained volunteers to visit newly transferred patients and to
offer support and friendship to help them feel at home in their
new environments.

Contact with the Judson Memorial Church led to the
church's offer to provide furnished office space and three-
months' free use of a telephone. Other small individual contributions provided operational support. The primary resource,
however, has been the volunteer work of Ms. Ann Wyatt, a
social worker. Other special assistance has come from Mr. Irv-
ing Weisenfeld, a former licensed nursing home administrator
who joined the Gray Panthers in order to find an effective way
to help reform nursing home conditions.

The group developed basic training materials and experi-
mented with video-taping their training sessions for use in
other settings. It has concentrated on sensitizing volunteers to
special concerns of patients and communication problems. The
training program included a workshop on hearing impairment
and communication difficulties by an audiologist from Columbia University's audiology department.

In September 1975 the group became actively involved in
advocacy for patients being transferred from a Greenwich Village nursing home. The state health department had directed
the home to transfer over one hundred residents because of
overcrowded, unsafe conditions.

It became clear to the Gray Panthers, who had been sending
volunteers to the home, that patients were being scheduled for
transfer without following any of the state rules and regulations. The group joined with the Consumer Commission for
the Accreditation of Health Services in making available to the
residents the service of Legal Services for the Elderly Poor. A

class action suit was brought on behalf of the patients to make sure that the state agencies protected their rights.

In order to offset action by the nursing home owner to close the entire facility and transfer all the residents, the Gray Panthers helped organize a community group, the Ad Hoc Committee to Save the Village Nursing Home. The Committee decided to approach the local community hospital, St. Vincent's, in hopes of persuading them to take over administration of the facility on a volunteer basis. Due to tremendous community response, the state health department and St. Vincent's began active negotiations. In the meantime, the court extended the restraining order against the transfer of residents until early December to enable negotiations to continue.

In December, Project Remember was called into action again when another local nursing home began transferring patients without regard to their individual rights. In a joint letter to the Moreland Act Commission, a state nursing home investigative unit created by Governor Carey, the Gray Panthers and the Consumer Commission for the Accreditation of Health Services outlined in detail the horrendous manner in which patients were being transferred. They faulted the state departments of health and social services as well as the nursing home administration. Their letter reported that "representatives from other homes were coming to the facility to pick out the patients they believed would require the least care." The letter continued, "It was described by a professional staff member . . . as 'body-snatching.' " They also reported patients being moved after five minutes notice and moved without medical records or provision for medical follow-up.

Once again, the groups called for assistance from Legal Services for the Elderly Poor, who successfully petitioned for a restraining order on behalf of patients.

The staff and volunteers of the New York Gray Panther group worked effectively for passage of a progressive legislative package in New York. They have advised and motivated local coalitions and monitored state regulatory action regarding resident transfers. Their information and expertise have been used by the Moreland Act Commission. Through all this, their primary focus has been monitoring the individual rights of residents through committed volunteer work.

Citizens for Better Nursing Home Care, Inc.
Mr. Allan Hahn, Chairman
P.O. Box 90920
Milwaukee, Wisconsin 53202   (414) 224-0460

Citizens for Better Nursing Home Care organized after a
small group of state and county government employees concluded that they were having little impact on solving nursing
home problems through their government positions. They
recognized the need for a community organization politically
separate from bureaucracy blocking reform. CBNHC was incorporated as a nonprofit organization in May 1975.

The group has received primary support, including office
space and use of a telephone from the Council on Urban Life
of the Milwaukee Catholic Archdiocese. Consultation with
members of CBNHC moved the council to publish a special
report, "Nursing Homes . . . Through the Looking Glass" in
March 1975. The council also published the CBNHC pamphlet
"Nursing Homes: How to Avoid if You Can: How to Select
if You Must." This shoppers' guide to home care services and
nursing homes lists things to look for when considering a nursing home, and tells what to do if care is not adequate.

Mr. Allan Hahn, CBNHC chairman, and Mr. Maurice Nin-
ham, both employees of a local welfare agency, are working
with others to provide an ongoing record of conditions in local
nursing homes. Funding attempts include submission of a
special project proposal to the local commission on aging to
set up an information and referral system on local nursing
homes and alternative types of care.

Another project has attempted to influence the local comprehensive health planning agency to develop and provide a
mechanism for citizen input in reviewing applications for facility construction or expansion.

In other action, CBNHC is represented on a committee
drawing up guidelines to improve survey procedures in a local
suburb which has its own nursing home ordinance.

The Council on Urban Life has assigned a staff person to
work full time with CBNHC. In addition, the group asks for
a one-time membership fee of $5.00 from those who can
afford it. Paid members number approximately sixty, although
supportive citizens number many more.

Seagull Volunteer Program
Contact: Ms. Dorothea R. Reaves
3637 N.E. First Avenue
Miami, Florida 33137 (305) 573-4050

In 1973 Protestant Social Services in Miami surveyed forty-four local nursing homes to determine whether religious services were being conducted and whether the services of trained volunteers were desired. The survey revealed limited volunteer programs; and the organization began the Seagull Volunteer Program.

The goals were generally outlined to be the enrichment of the residents' lives, increased community awareness, and involvement of the public in improving patient care.

A substantial training program for volunteers was established. The ten-hour program includes sessions on common physical problems of older people, myths and attitudes on aging, surveillance of nursing homes, death and dying, sexuality in the nursing home, and legal considerations for confined persons.

The program emphasis has been to find volunteers who can meet the individual needs of residents, e.g., Spanish-speaking persons, and men to relate to male residents.

Assistance has come from many local churches and from students of the Barry College School of Social Work. One graduate student did a special study to measure the effectiveness of young volunteers as compared to older volunteers.

In January 1976 the group had recruited, trained, and certified a corps of 368 volunteers. Seventy-eight were high school students; ten volunteers were over eighty.

Arrangements have been made for training sessions to be rotated in nursing homes throughout Miami-Dade County. Local churches and organizations "host" a volunteer program, including the job of motivating and enlisting a minimum of twenty interested persons.

Every group or nursing home participating in the program has special guidelines outlined for them in a booklet provided by Protestant Social Services. Certified Seagulls are also given a special guide to supplement their orientation and training.

In each of the twenty-two nursing homes participating in the program, a volunteer "leader" is responsible for channeling resident concerns to appropriate channels. If major problems

arise which cannot be handled in the home, they are referred
to a special review team set up by the program to handle problems impartially.

Northwest Interfaith Movement
Contact: Mr. Donald Scott
Greene Street at Westview
Philadelphia, Pennsylvania 19119   (215) 843-5600

In 1974, the Northwest Interfaith Movement (NIM), a coalition of community churches and synagogues in the north-
western area of Philadelphia, initiated a nursing home action
project through its older adults task force. NIM is a cooperative community project that serves as a link between community needs and community resources. The organization acts as
a catalyst in developing education and action programs dealing
with community problems felt to be most damaging to human
values and human potential.

The nursing home project began by training thirty-five volunteers to make team investigative visits to nursing homes in
northwest Philadelphia. The survey results revealed a great
need to improve conditions in local homes, and led to a community symposium on nursing home care. The formation of a
volunteer friendly visitor program followed. In 1975, NIM
organized and conducted a series of training programs for volunteer visitors who now regularly visit thirteen nursing homes
in the area.

Another approach by NIM has been to meet with nursing
home administrators and activity directors to establish a working dialogue and promote new programs and services. An active relationship with one activity director led to a horticulture
therapy program. The project has also explored the role of the
nurse aides to assess their potential impact for providing quality care.

One of the most exciting and successful accomplishments of
the nursing home action project resulted from a meeting with
the clergy of greater Germantown. During the discussion, the
idea emerged of congregations "adopting" a nursing home. In
the "Adopt-a-Home" plan, members of a church form a friendly visitor program for one nursing home. NIM acts as a catalyst
by publicizing the program to community churches. Once a

church shows interest, NIM initiates negotiations to implement a program between the church and a local nursing home. NIM also enlists the support and involvement of various community resource persons with expertise in long-term care. The resource persons help plan and prepare strategies to remedy problems as well as train volunteers. By December 1975 four local congregations had "adopted a home" and several others had expressed interest. NIM is hopeful that at a later stage churches and volunteers can also take a more active advocacy role.

NIM's members and resource people are all volunteers. As the program has grown, however, the need for a staff person to coordinate activities has been recognized. NIM submitted a funding proposal to a local foundation which would enable it to hire a coordinator to work eight hours a week. NIM also plans to use two social welfare and urban studies field placement students from a nearby college to assist them part-time in planning and implementing their nursing home activities.

Minneapolis Age and Opportunity Center, Inc.
Mrs. Daphne Krause, Executive Director
1801 Nicollet Avenue South
Minneapolis, Minnesota 55403 (612) 874-5525

The Minneapolis Age and Opportunity Center is a nonprofit organization managed by senior citizens. MAO was organized to establish alternative programs to prevent unnecessary institutionalization of the elderly. Early in its development, the senior citizen leadership requested the director, Mrs. Daphne Krause, to conduct an investigation of the state's nursing homes. MAO had received a great number of nursing home complaints, many related to the same facilities. Mrs. Krause began her investigation in 1970. She asked complainants to write to the state health department and began collecting sworn affidavits documenting abuses. Nursing home employees, primarily nurse aides and orderlies, who brought complaints to MAO were asked to continue their employment in the facility and accurately document abuses. After three years of investigation and public hearings, MAO testified before a hearing of the Senate Special Committee on Aging held in Minnesota. Their testimony, outlining abuses against patients, presented a powerful indictment of substandard facilities. MAO has been successful in its lobbying efforts to improve state rules and regulations and to increase the number of state inspectors. New regulations include a patients' bill of rights, a provision requiring one or more unannounced inspections, and creation of a citation system.

Denver Gray Panthers
Contact: Mr. Duane Gall
1400 Lafayette
Denver, Colorado 80218   (303) 832-5618

The Denver Gray Panthers organized their nursing home task force in the summer of 1974. The group immediately recognized the need to provide specific consumer information about Denver metropolitan area nursing homes. A special survey questionnaire was developed and mailed to administrators in all Denver nursing homes. Fifty-five of eighty facilities responded. Task force members followed up the mail survey with personal visits to each home, interviewing residents, administrators, and staff. Although very valuable information was obtained, the task force decided against publishing a consumer guide for two major reasons: there was little standardization of information and conditions of each nursing home were changing too rapidly. All survey results, however, are on file at the Gray Panther office and are available for public review.

In May 1975, the group received a $2,700 contract grant from the HEW regional Office of Long-Term Care Standards Enforcement Division to hold two workshops on consumer advocacy in nursing homes. The objectives were to provide consumers with solid background information about nursing homes and to suggest direct action projects citizens might become involved in to improve the long-term care system. The workshops were held in the fall of 1975. The training grant proposal and contract developed by the Denver group can be used as a model by other citizen groups.

The Gerus Society
Contact: Mr. Bruce Sneath
840 South Carondelet
Los Angeles, California 90057 (213) 385-4704

The Gerus Society is a reform group sponsored by the Church of Scientology. In 1975 the Society began a persistent campaign to improve nursing home conditions. The campaign began in California where they investigated facilities in the Los Angeles area. The investigation resulted in the publication of several special reports. One report, *Rewards of Old Age Expanded*, covered extensive abuses in local nursing homes and "locked" facilities. In *The Cost of Reform*, the Society focused on money spent on improper, inadequate care, and profiteering.

In August 1975 the Society presented a special report, *Quality of Care: Nursing Home Care in Los Angeles County* to the governor, the state department of health, and California state legislators. The report detailed deficiencies and abuses the group found in one local nursing home. The abuses were thoroughly documented and the facility was named. Recommendations focused on corrective measures for that facility and steps for improving the general quality of care in similar facilities. As part of the strategy, the Society included a petition signed by 2,500 citizens demanding that the governor halt the use of tranquilizing drugs as a means of controlling patients in nursing homes.

The Gerus Society's focus is similar to the Church of Scientology's: a critical blast at psychiatric and mental health care in America. The Society also zeroes in on major nursing home problems and supports general reform actions of citizen action groups.

The campaign for nursing home reform has spread to Society branches in other cities and states. In Maryland they have conducted a special survey to determine the extent of institutional abuses.

The New England Elderly Demands Society (NEEDS), a society branch in Boston, was organized in the summer of 1974. NEEDS operates on the premise that the general public has not been aware of treatment given to older people in institutions, nor has it known about federal and state policies governing the operation of long-term care facilities.

NEEDS undertook a ten-month research study which included a statewide survey, visiting nursing homes, interviewing nursing home residents and their relatives and friends, as well as investigating government agencies and other groups having influence over the long-term care system.

Their work resulted in three documentary reports in 1975, titled *The Institutional Elderly: Human or Animal?* The first deals with overall nursing home problems as well as a brief discussion of innovations in long-term care. The second is based on survey results in which residents were asked what ought to be done to improve conditions. The third discusses government expenditures under the current system and briefly describes the basic alternatives to institutionalization.

NEEDS is beginning to move into an active legislative role, contacting legislators to advocate reform.

Kansas City Gray Panthers
Geriatric Aide Training Program
Mrs. Mildred Barnes, Director
2937 Lockridge
Kansas City, Missouri 64128

Fifteen years ago Mrs. Mildred Barnes received a sketchy training and orientation program as preparation for her new responsibilities as a nurse aide in a local Kansas City hospital. Now in 1975, she finds herself the creator, organizer, and director of the geriatric-aide training program which has evolved from her activities with the Kansas City Gray Panther Home Health Committee.

Mrs. Barnes contends that one of the reasons the nursing home industry has not provided a level of care expected by the public is inadequately trained personnel. Although there are a few general nurse aide training programs in local hospitals and nursing homes in the Kansas City area, no training programs had been designed or implemented specifically for the role of geriatric nurse aid. Mrs. Barnes and a twenty-two-member advisory board began to plan a program. A funding proposal for a geriatric-aide training program was prepared and submitted to the Human Development Division of Catholic Family Charity as well as the local CETA program. In designing the curriculum, the planning committee used a format developed by organizations such as the American Red Cross, the American Health Care Association, and the Missouri state department of health. The course plan includes two hundred hours of classroom work and actual clinical experience at a local nursing home. It will introduce students to the psychological, physiological, and sociological aspects of the aging process. A significant part of the course pertains to agist attitudes. Special emphasis will be placed on patients' rights.

A broad base of community support has been developed through an advisory board composed of representatives of community and church organizations, members of health professions, including physicians, nurses, nurse aides, and nursing home administrators; as well as consumers and senior citizens.

Friends and Relatives of Nursing Home Patients, Inc.
Contact: Mrs. Ruth Shepherd
1765 East 26th
Eugene, Oregon 97403

Friends and Relatives is a statewide consumer group in Oregon whose primary interest is to represent nursing home residents. The volunteer group, established in 1972, resulted from a recommendation of the governor's nursing home task force. The key organizer, Mrs. Ruth Shepherd, had been a member of that task force.

The awesome organizational objective of Friends and Relatives is to include in its membership at least one family member or friend who is legally or financially responsible for each resident in long-term care facilities across the state. According to Mrs. Shepherd, no one can speak better for older patients than friends and relatives who really care. Membership, however, is open to all persons and organizations.

Testimony before the governor's task force had indicated a pressing need for public information on selecting and evaluating nursing homes. Consequently, one of the first goals was to prepare a "Guide to Oregon's Nursing Homes."

A survey form was mailed to each nursing home in the state. Amazingly, the group had obtained funds for the mailing from the Oregon Health Care Association (the state nursing home association). According to Mrs. Shepherd, the association could hardly refuse after they had publicly claimed that their facilities were open, that they were truly concerned with improving the quality of care.

Friends and Relatives planned to publish the guide if the survey responses totaled fifty percent or better. Unfortunately, only forty percent responded, so it was not published. The group still plans to produce a consumer guide when adequate resources become available.

The organization has served as an information, education, referral, and complaint center. When complaints are received, Friends and Relatives assists the individual in filing a formal complaint with the health department. It then monitors action on the complaint.

The group has been successful in lobbying before county and state boards as well as the state legislature. During the 1973 legislative session, Friends and Relatives opposed a bill introduced by the Department of Human Resources, which if passed, would have denied the public access to nursing home complaint files. The bill was defeated. The group strongly supported a bill, introduced by the House Committee on Aging, requiring a minimum of one unannounced nursing home inspection per year. The bill was passed in the 1975 session.

Nursing Home Consumers Group
Mr. Peter Stathopoulos, Chairperson
c/o Mental Health Center
Nichols Road
Fitchburg, Massachusetts 01420 (617) 343-6966

The Nursing Home Consumers Group was precipitated by the activities of the North Central Massachusetts Mental Health Center. Mr. William Aliski and other professional staff at the center had become concerned about the release of residents from mental hospitals into local nursing homes. They wanted assurance that these persons were placed in homes providing good care, and they were concerned about the total mental health needs of community residents in need of long-term care.

The group's first meeting in October 1974 was attended by five community people interested in nursing homes. They felt that with time and effort, they could become advocates for all patients in nursing homes and that their interest, if supported by community agencies, would stimulate change and reform. They met monthly in an effort to clarify issues, discuss problems, formulate plans, and generally become more knowledgeable about nursing home care.

The group now has approximately fifty members, mostly older people or relatives of nursing home residents, but it also includes residents, young people, former nursing home employees, and agency representatives. Providers, such as social workers or administrators, may join but do not have voting privileges.

One of the primary activities is providing information to the public. The group contends there has been no formal mechanism for families or individuals to use to obtain information about nursing homes or about rules and regulations. They believe people need a credible, responsible alternative to organized industry interests and to the limited, sometimes obscure responses of the government regulatory agencies.

The group has supported progressive state legislation and a program of local senior-citizen ombudsmen. It has received nursing home complaints from residents' families. In an effort to begin investigations and resolve problems, it has been meetings with the state attorney general's office and a local Legal Aid attorney. In June 1975 the group sponsored a successful "Consumer Conference on Nursing Homes," attended by over one hundred community people, agency representatives, and representatives of the news media.

Special Friends
Mrs. Helen Chesterman, R.N., Chairperson
2324 Funston Avenue
San Francisco, California 94116

The sparkplug behind this group is Mrs. Helen Chesterman, a retired registered nurse and former Director of Public Health Nursing in the San Francisco Department of Public Health. In 1973, Mrs. Chesterman was asked to visit a woman in a nursing home. She was appalled at what she saw and decided that lonely people in nursing homes needed someone to visit and care for them and to act as their advocates. She began organizing her friends, many of whom were retired nurses, and the new informal group began to "adopt" nursing home patients.

By 1975, approximately thirty-five people were regularly
visiting residents on a one-to-one basis and were meeting together monthly to discuss their experiences and concerns.

Mrs. Chesterman drafted her own patients' bill of rights and
a guide for volunteer visitors. The group has worked closely
with other concerned organizations, such as the American
Association of Retired Persons, the RSVP, the Council of
Churches, and the local and state nurses' associations.

Special Friends has had considerable press coverage which
has helped in recruiting volunteer visitors. In 1975, a San Francisco newspaper named Mrs. Chesterman one of the year's
"Ten Most Distinguished Women" for founding Special
Friends. Currently, the group is seeking established community organizations or agencies to assist in administration and
funding. Operating expenses have been paid out of the pockets
of volunteers.

Public Interest Research Groups
(See Resources section for a list of
nursing home reports published by PIRGs)

In 1971, students in Minnesota and Oregon organized the
first Public Interest Research Groups (PIRG). The groups were
based on an idea suggested by Ralph Nader that students could
perform a service to society and gain a practical education by
working through student-funded and directed PIRGs. By 1975
there were PIRGs in 23 states and the District of Columbia,
supported by more than 500,000 members who contribute
combined revenues of over $1.4 million annually. The Citizens
Action Group (CAG), the organizing arm of Nader's Public
Citizen, has helped create and train public interest advocacy
groups at community and state levels and CAG coordinates
the activities of the PIRGs.

In 1974, four student PIRGs conducted major nursing home
studies, issued reports recommending action for change, and
lobbied for legislative reform. The Oregon PIRG study offers
an overview of the state's nursing homes and the relationships
between the facilities and regulatory agencies. Major areas of
concern were: compliance with regulations; staff education;
representation for residents; and the financial status of nursing
homes.

The Iowa PIRG's fourteen-month statewide investigation was done by more than fifty people. It provided an overview of current conditions and the regulatory system responsible for enforcing minimum standards. The final report points the way to constructive steps both providers and consumers can take to upgrade facilities and offers recommendations to facilitate enforcement of minimum standards.

The Maine PIRG was spurred to action when a patient's bill of rights failed to be considered by the legislature. The nursing home study centered around that issue. A survey determined the extent to which common complaints against nursing homes were exceptions or the rule and pinpointed factors causing the nursing home patient's isolation.

The Connecticut PIRG studied thirty-eight chronic and convalescent nursing homes located in the capital region. It included an investigation of state regulatory agencies and a review of official inspection reports. Student investigators visited each facility, validating deficiencies and assessing the attitudes of the administrator and staff.

Santa Clara Valley Coalition
Nursing Home Task Force
Mrs. Mabel Brown, Coordinator
2435 Forest Avenue
San Jose, CA 95128 (408) 248-6736

In 1974 Mabel Brown, now the coordinator of the nursing home task force, became interested in nursing homes as a result of complaints to the office of the California state assemblyman where she worked. A preliminary survey of community organizations indicated that many people were concerned about nursing home problems and most felt powerless to do anything about them. Organizational work led to a joint investigative project supported by the Public Interest Law Center, a nonprofit organization doing public interest research and litigation; the Barristers Club, part of the county bar association whose members are attorneys under thirty-five; and the Santa Clara Valley Coalition, a consortium of citizen interest groups.

In May 1975, the group released a major investigative report, *Nursing Home Care in California: A Santa Clara Case Study*, to the governor and the state department of health. The thirty-five-member group consisted of private citizens, professionals who had worked or were working in nursing homes, young lawyers, and law students. They had interviewed patients, employees, administrators, former employees, and relatives of patients, as well as doing on-site investigations in twenty-five facilities.

The report listed atrocities in local nursing homes, but did not name the facilities. The primary purpose was to bring the problems to the attention of government officials and regulatory agencies, demanding that serious questions be answered through official investigation. Questions such as: How is money presently appropriated to our state's nursing homes spent? Where does it go? What does it buy? Who owns the businesses with which nursing homes themselves do business? What is the extent of Medi-Cal (Medicaid) fraud? What is the extent of patient trust fund mismanagement?

A task force delegation personally presented the report to the director of the state health department and the deputy secretary of the state health and welfare agency. The release of the report at a press conference in the state's capital led to nine major newspaper stories. The report received immediate recognition and a promise for action from the progressive director of the health department, Dr. Jerome Lackner. In a virtually unprecedented reaction from a governmental agency, he responded in writing that within six months he would investigate all the homes visited by the task force. Furthermore, he stated, "I would welcome any member of your group accompanying our evaluators as observers during these inspections."

Even the industry trade association, the California Association of Health Facilities (CAHF), immediately issued a press release which stated support for several of the group's recommendations.

The task force did not stop with taking its recommendations directly to the state director of the health department. In June they took their concerns to a meeting of the Santa Clara County Board of Supervisors. At that meeting the board adopted a resolution in support of the task force recommendations and agreed to forward the resolution to the governor.

In July task force members met with their district attorney to explore ways that the office could be more active in investigating and prosecuting nursing home violators. Following a pledge to the task force, District Attorney Louis Bergna appointed a deputy to evaluate complaints of criminal conduct in nursing home facilities. In a joint press release with the district attorney's office announcing this action, the task force established its own hotline to receive citizen complaints about nursing home problems.

By that time the task force had already arranged for people to accompany the special evaluating teams of the state health department and had sent representatives to participate in the department's training sessions on new regulations.

That same month the group met with the department's chief of licensing to press for his commitment to work with the district attorney. They urged that they be invited to participate in training sessions for nursing home administrators. These and other demands and questions were formulated in writing before the meeting and presented to the licensure chief in order to assure answers.

In September, the task force organized a special session in Sacramento with the director of the state department of health and the attorney general. They were successful in bringing over three hundred persons to Sacramento in five chartered buses. At the meeting the task force made six demands:

(1) Cooperation from the local health department, which had not been forthcoming;

(2) Redistricting and strengthening local inspection areas: inspectors to work from a manageable geographical area and local offices to have power to levy fines and refuse licensure; inspection teams to be supplemented by special trouble-shooting teams;

(3) Re-evaluation of department of health administrative personnel. The task force questioned their competence, qualifications and attitudes. They offered criteria for an evaluation and recommended that the director "transfer, promote, terminate, and hire personnel at all levels" to assure high quality and public accountability;

(4) A coherent plan to be developed and implemented in three weeks, to reduce the time period for revoking licenses;

(5) Medi-Cal audits with consumer input; and the reason a $2-a-day increase had been authorized in Medi-Cal rates prior to audits of all nursing homes to determine costs;

(6) Special training seminars for consumers on the new regulations and patients' rights.

In September, task force members met with five health department representatives to discuss progress in their joint surveillance of fourteen selected county facilities. The task force announced plans to accompany evaluators in follow-up visits to facilities under scrutiny. Plans were finalized for unannounced follow-up visits to start in October and a volunteer coordinator was appointed for those visits.

In October, Dr. Lackner announced that the Nursing Home Task Force of the Santa Clara Valley Coalition would serve as a consumer watchdog over nursing home matters and submit an official monthly report to his office. As part of this report he asked for a written critique of the department's performance in licensing and inspecting nursing homes. He reported, "Government officials perform best when citizen groups cooperate by helping us monitor our programs, by making constructive criticisms and the continuous checks required to ensure that we bureaucrats are doing our best to fulfill the spirit of the law."

Also in October, the task force began special efforts to make the local comprehensive health planning agency responsive to quality care for nursing home residents. When the agency overlooked task force recommendations regarding one local facility, the task force admonished the agency in writing and questioned "the accountability of the board to the public."

In subsequent regular meetings with state health department staff, the task force pushed for nursing home evaluators to work on their professional relationships with administrators and staff of facilities. They also called for a system in which various teams of evaluators would be rotated within their respective districts, as we have noted, to prevent the attitude of "These are my facilities" and the special friendships that feeling encourages.

In January, the task force and the state health department jointly sponsored a "Community Action Workshop" to explore such issues as: How do you choose a nursing home? What are your rights in nursing homes? What do we do about problems? How do we organize for change? Over three hundred persons attended the workshop.

At the workshop people were given special handouts developed by the Senior Citizens Law Program of the California Rural Legal Assistance Office on how to complain effectively. Particular emphasis was placed on obtaining support for a state demonstration project to show how elderly people can remain out of institutions through an alternative care system.

In an exceptional action at the workshop, the task force demanded an immediate answer from the state health director and the secretary of health and welfare as to why three named state agency employees should not be called upon to resign or be replaced. The task force made charges against the three employees including "a total lack of willingness and ability to cooperate with the task force," and of "misdirected loyalty towards the industry."

Although the task force has remained highly critical of government agencies, the unique receptiveness of certain high officials has assured continuing dialogue and noticeable government action.

Nursing Home Campaign Committee, Inc.
Mrs. Elizabeth Maier, President
1547 Pratt Street
Philadelphia, Pennsylvania 19124 (215) 744-0882

In June 1970, forty older people representing thirty-five senior citizen clubs met at a special five-day seminar to discuss problems faced by older people. The primary problem brought to the attention of the group was conditions suffered by patients in the city's nursing homes. The seminar resulted in the formation of the Nursing Home Campaign Committee, which elected as chairman Mrs. Elizabeth Maier, one of the older persons concerned about the issue. The new group decided to give correction of nursing home problems top priority and they began immediately to mobilize the community.

Knowing that many nursing and boarding home residents had no family or friends as visitors, NHCC's first major effort was to organize a friendly visitor program. The group also knew that residents who had regular visitors were usually treated with more respect and consideration by nursing home personnel and were less likely to be victims of abuse.

The group began recruiting volunteers through community organizations, churches, senior citizen groups, local high schools and colleges, sororities and fraternities. A one-page flyer describing the visitor program was distributed throughout the community. Volunteers signed a "Cooperation Pledge,"

which indicated the facility to be visited, the approximate day
and time of each visit, and the kind of activity the volunteer
planned.

An investigative and advocacy function was added in November 1972. The committee prepared a "Visitors Report"
form for all volunteers. The visitor was asked to note the name
and address of the facility and the name of the patient visited,
as well as describe the patient's condition and any particular
needs the patient expressed or the visitor observed. The visitors were assured that patient names would be kept confidential. This provided a mechanism for documenting conditions
and served as a basis for further reform actions.

A primary tactic assuring a continual flow of volunteers has
been award luncheons where volunteers receive certificates for
their work. By 1975 NHCC had over two hundred volunteers
visiting nursing and boarding homes in the Philadelphia area.

In early 1973 the committee received a federal and state
grant through Title III of the Older Americans Act to develop
and operate a volunteer nursing home ombudsman project for
Philadelphia County. Through the committee's new office, the
ombudsman project was to receive, investigate, and attempt to
resolve patients' and relatives' complaints and grievances. The
project funds included a nominal amount to pay expenses of
the volunteer ombudsman.

The group produced complaint investigation forms and held
training sessions for volunteer ombudsmen. By September
1973 they had thirty-five volunteer ombudsmen investigating
and mediating complaints. During 1973, NHCC serviced over
1400 contacts for assistance and accepted 120 grievance cases.

In an effort to develop cooperation with the industry,
NHCC formed a committee with local nursing home administrators. They meet on a regular basis to discuss common problems and resolve grievances. Mrs. Maier believes that these
meetings opened doors to visitors and ombudsmen that might
otherwise have been closed. Further cooperation with the industry came about when the committee supported industry
requests for a higher Medicaid reimbursement rate.

In 1974 NHCC received second-year funding for the ombudsman program through the area agency on aging, the Philadelphia Corporation for the Aging (PCA). During two and one-
half years of operation, NHCC serviced 382 grievances. Its
application for 1975 funding from the PCA included 22 letters

of commendation from major local organizations involved in
the long-term care field. More than 100 letters were sent to
PCA in support of the ombudsman project. In September
1975, however, the committee received a letter advising them
that funding was being terminated because PCA funds were
not intended for the institutionalized elderly. NHCC pledged
that it would continue its service and began the struggle to obtain funds from other sources.

In the spring of 1974, NHCC began a vigorous campaign to
provide better care and increase the number of available beds
for Medicaid recipients. They lobbied state and local officials
to support action by the city government to renovate and
establish a nursing home on state-owned property. There were
three objectives: to provide placement for patients relocated
from substandard facilities; to make available places for Medicaid patients refused placement by other nursing homes; and to
provide competition to spur better conditions in the existing
facilities.

NHCC submitted petitions with over 25,000 signatures supporting their stand. Mrs. Maier and other volunteers personally
visited the facility, the Landis State Hospital, a building unused for over a year, and found it acceptable. In a letter to the
governor advising him of her visit, Mrs. Maier remarked,
". . . and when I think and visualize the horrible places in
which many of our elderly ill exist — while this building goes
unused — I am appalled."

Because of bureaucratic redtape and snaillike action, the
city does not plan to open the facility until 1977. NHCC
wants it opened earlier and is now seeking assistance from
other community organizations and senior citizen clubs to
force the issue.

In its continual efforts to promote better care for patients,
NHCC mobilizes letter campaigns to elected city, county, and
state officials, and uses direct confrontation when necessary. It
is not uncommon for members to sit for hours in officials'
offices waiting for an opportunity to present their views directly. NHCC is a member of a powerful senior citizen advocacy group, the Action Alliance of Philadelphia, and receives
substantial support from the coalition's leadership and members.

Typical of Mrs. Maier's sustained leadership and philosophy
is her statement in one of her monthly mailings to supporters:

"I realize that I am only one of the 1,025,000 voters in Philadelphia and only one of the many thousands of senior citizens in our City. However, we are all traveling the same road and any one of us may one day be in the position of the many elderly ill who need nursing home beds today — many never expected to be in that position."

Since the loss of its major funding source, NHCC has solicited and received cash donations from individual older people and senior citizen organizations. One local group organized a bingo and card party to raise money to help keep the organization going. Membership dues have been a small source of support from the beginning. Individuals pay $2.00; groups pay more according to their size. NHCC solicits "contributing memberships" for $25.00.

There is little doubt that Mrs. Maier's group will survive. Its members are committed advocates for nursing home patients. For example, in response to a recent photo and newspaper article, she commended Mayor Frank Rizzo on his highly publicized personal visit to the site of an oil slick, where he voiced concern for wild geese. Her letter noted that she would very much like to see him in a photo standing beside one of the city's deplorable boarding homes voicing similar concern for the old folks.

Citizens for the Improvement of Nursing Homes, Inc.
Mrs. Dorothy Kallgren, President
9103 32nd Avenue, N.E.
Seattle, Washington 98115

Citizens for the Improvement of Nursing Homes, Inc., began with five people meeting together in 1969 to discuss the possibility of united action to improve conditions in nursing homes. One of the organizers, Mrs. Helen Anthony, had witnessed poor and abusive care of a person in a nursing home and felt that someday she too might be in that position. Another organizer, Mrs. Dorothy Kallgren, a retired secretary and bookkeeper, was then a shy person, afraid of public speaking. Today she is the president of this organization representing over three thousand individuals and is noted statewide for her expertise and advocacy work for nursing home patients.

Reflecting on the beginning of CINH, the organizers say that had they known at that time the immensity of the problems and the complexity of the system, they might have been too discouraged to continue their efforts. By working together, however, they were able to interest other individuals with similar concerns.

By June 1970 CINH incorporated as a nonprofit organization. In September 1971 they issued their first newsletter. In this way, the organization has been able to reach a larger audience.

One of the first problems the group faced was internal; its members were, for the most part, elderly people fearful of the future. Unequipped for leadership, they tended to lean on those who were strong and a feeling of being "locked in" pervaded the newly established CINH Board. In an effort to break loose, an attempt was made to form a nursing home coalition with other community groups, but support was lacking.

CINH has been successful, however, in the role of ombudsman and advocate, receiving and mediating nursing home complaints in the Seattle-King County area. The process of complaint investigation and subsequent resolution serves two functions: it ameliorates a problem for one or more patients in a nursing home while it provides the organization with specific data to determine the kinds of actions necessary to avoid similar situations. By handling complaints, the group learns what legislative direction must be pursued and what recommendations must be made to regulatory agencies in order to bring about needed changes in policy and regulations.

The group soon realized they could not operate an effective ombudsman office without better funding. The $2.00-per-year membership dues and the limited donations cannot sustain their many activities and currently CINH is submitting a grant proposal to HEW for funds to establish a statewide nursing home ombudsman program.

It is strategically important for any consumer group to become active in the political and legislative arena. This is a point that Mrs. Kallgren stresses, and this strategy has produced a remarkable effect for CINH. The group has learned that even a small organization, if well informed and carefully structured, can succeed where a larger, unwieldy one might fail.

A major CINH accomplishment was successful lobbying which resulted in the passage of a bill requiring complete nursing home financial disclosure and a bill requiring public disclosure of nursing home inspection reports. In 1973, CINH began a major lobbying effort to introduce legislation to establish a citation system for nursing homes in violation of federal rules and regulations. CINH was primarily responsible for drafting the bill, locating and winning the support of sponsors, and testifying at the legislative hearings. The bill, introduced in 1974, did not get out of committee. Intensified CINH lobbying efforts led to passage of the bill in the 1975 legislative session.

Another facet of the CINH strategy has been to gain appointments to key governmental advisory boards and planning committees. The group has its representatives on various county and state boards having jurisdiction over nursing homes. The CINH president is now serving in a key position as a member of the State Nursing Home Administrators Licensing Board. In addition the group has established a working relationship with the Office of Nursing Home Affairs of the Department of Social and Health Services and has asked to be included in any meetings the department or the regional HEW office holds with representatives of the nursing home industry, and thus far this request has been met. Having representatives in meetings in these key positions has a salutary effect; the nursing home industry now acknowledges CINH as a formidable adversary.

CINH is currently exposing instances of misappropriation of patients' personal trust fund accounts by nursing home owners and is urging state and regional investigations by appropriate agencies. Investigative research is being conducted by the CINH membership on nursing home ownership patterns. A statement CINH has filed with the state attorney general points out that "physician ownership in long-term care facilities in combination with treatment of patients by the doctor is a dangerous conflict of interest." CINH has also distributed copies of the patients' rights regulations and urges persons aware of violations of the rights to report them either to CINH or the Social Security office.

Citizens for the Improvement of Nursing Homes
Spokane Branch
Contact: Mrs. Marion Ballentine
4128 North Wall Street
Spokane, Washington 99205

The Spokane branch of CINH was formally initiated in September 1975 following a conference entitled "Nursing Home Dilemma," with representatives of the Seattle CINH as program participants. Over one hundred people attended this public meeting which attracted newspaper, television, radio, and wire service coverage: the kind of media attention that makes professional public relations agencies drool.

The organizer and driving force behind the Spokane branch is a retired schoolteacher, Mrs. Marion Ballentine, who had actually begun a one-woman crusade about eight months earlier. Prior to that time, Mrs. Ballentine confesses, she had never heard of CINH. She hadn't realized the extent of problems in nursing homes as she had never seen any criticism of nursing homes in the Spokane newspapers and she had never dreamed of ever doing anything like leading a meeting. In fact, she had just learned the afghan stitch and was ready to settle into the stereotyped role of an "old lady."

Mrs. Ballentine was moved to action when she came in touch with a fifty-five-year old nurse aide who had attempted to commit suicide and learned from her that the wages for nurse aides were only two dollars an hour. After six years of working, this aide had no salary increases and no fringe benefits. Mrs. Ballentine was infuriated. Through the National Organization for Women's Task Force on Older Women, she initiated a local study of the wage situation which convinced her that the below-poverty wages are at the root of all problems with nursing homes.

No Spokane nursing home had been unionized. When she talked with aides, she found they were totally unaware of union possibilities. Several attempts to organize the health workers into an effective bargaining and lobbying force were instituted: she contacted the Service Employees Union to attempt to activate them; she ran an ad in the local paper to help initiate an organizing drive. Dozens of nursing home employees responded to the ad, but the union did not have sufficient staff to assist in the organizing.

A second major plan of attack against the low wages was directed toward church-affiliated nursing homes, which also exploit women who work as aides. Mrs. Ballentine's study showed church-related homes paid the same low wages as proprietary homes, and she began a letter-writing campaign to all administrators and boards, appealing to them to set an example by increasing the salaries of their employees.

The Spokane branch of CINH now has thirty members. Like the Seattle branch, they too act as an ombudsman. In July 1975, they ran an ad in the "Personals" column for ten days at a cost of forty dollars. The ad, which read: "CINH is now receiving nursing home complaints" and listed a name and phone number, resulted in over 150 complaints from nursing home personnel and family and friends of nursing home residents. Some nursing home personnel continue to carry the phone number to give to friends or relatives who wish to register a complaint.

Mrs. Ballentine assists individual complainants by formally preparing a written letter detailing the complaint and forwarding the letter to the state department of social and health services. About ten copies are sent to other agencies and key officials who have some jurisdictional responsibilities for nursing homes.

Lack of funding is a continuous problem. The increasing visibility of CINH in the community has resulted in an increased demand for services and a heavier work load. The Spokane branch has $1.25 membership dues, but the majority of the operating expense for phone calls, mailings, traveling, etc., has come from the personal pocket of the retired organizer.

National Council of Senior Citizens
Nursing Home Information Center
Volunteer Staff: Mrs. Annabelle Seidman
1511 "K" Street, N.W.
Washington, D.C. 20024 (202) 783-6850

In May 1974 the Washington, D.C., chapter of the National Consumers League opened its demonstration, consumer-oriented Health Service Information Center. The first of its kind in the United States, the center made available to the public a centralized file of government inspection reports of Medicare-reimbursable nursing homes in the metropolitan area.

In the fall of 1975, the inspection reports and files of the League's information center were transferred to the headquarters of the National Council of Senior Citizens. The project is being continued and expanded as the Nursing Home Information Center with the volunteer help of Mrs. Annabelle Seidman, a former volunteer with the National Consumers League who was instrumental in the development of their information center.

In fact, the information collecting began in January 1973 when the Medicare and Medicaid nursing home inspection reports became public information, Mr. Mal Schecter, chairman of the League's Health Consumer Action Program and Washington editor of *Hospital Practice*, was concerned about the application of the Freedom of Information Act. He visited a Social Security district office to review the inspection reports.

Schecter found that only a summary of each inspection report was available at the local office. It took from two to four weeks to obtain the full report, which he had to order from the regional HEW office. When the full reports arrived, he compared them with the summaries and noted that much valuable information was lost in the summarizing process. Furthermore, each local Social Security office only had the inspection reports for facilities in its district; he had to visit several offices to obtain information on all nursing homes in the District of Columbia.

The League agreed with Schecter; although there was a disclosure law with regulations, the information was not readily accessible to the average citizen looking for accurate information on which to base the selection of a nursing home. The idea of the Health Service Information Center emerged from this. The goal was to have the full inspection reports for all District nursing homes participating in the Medicaid reimbursement programs available to the public in one centralized location.

The project began by purchasing from the local Social Security and welfare offices a list of all nursing homes participating in the Medicare and Medicaid programs. Then they followed the procedure outlined in Chapter Three, submitting

written requests for the full inspection reports on facilities in
the Medicaid program to the local welfare office and to the
local Social Security office for facilities in Medicare. These
requests were then forwarded to the regional HEW office and
copies of the reports were made available. The League was
fortunate because the regional Social Security office repro-
duced, without charge, more than 1,500 pages which would
have cost $400 to copy. (A full inspection report is approxi-
mately 60 pages; at the current rate of 10¢ a page, copying
costs about $6 a report, and if a facility has been inspected
more than once the previous year, there will be more than one
report for that facility. You can, however, review the records
or copy them on your own machine *in* the local office without
charge or your local office may, like the League's Social Security office, waive or reduce the fee on the premise that disclosure of the information will be a primary benefit to the
general public.)

After obtaining all the full inspection reports, the League
decided to extract the most important information from the
full report and "The Summary of Deficiencies" in order to
compile a digest of consumer-related information for each
facility. The digest is a two-page mimeographed report
structured in a concise and easy-to-read form. The League
charged ten cents for each digest. Consumers have found it
useful because it can be taken along as they visit and compare
nursing homes in the area.

Because the center was designed as a demonstration project
with the hope that consumer groups in other cities would
establish similar programs, the League also prepared a manual
on how to establish an information center based on their
experiences. The manual includes development guidelines,
copies of the two issues of the *Federal Register* which detail
the rules and regulations for the disclosure of inspection
reports, the press release announcing the opening of the center, a sample of the official inspection summary, and a sample
copy of one of the center's digests of a full inspection report.

A first and important step for establishing an information
center is locating office space. The office should be large
enough to hold file cabinets, desk, telephone, and table and
chairs for visitors. Because many old people must rely on
public transportation, it is important that the center be located in an area readily accessible to public transportation.

The center can be staffed by one or two volunteers who are knowledgeable about nursing homes and can answer questions about the inspection reports.

The League organized a file folder on each of the nursing homes. Each folder contained the full inspection report, the deficiency summary, and the consumer digest. The League suggests that as the information center expands, additional information can be added to each file. Additional information may include: (1) comments from consumers who have visited the nursing home; (2) comments from owners or administrators of individual facilities; or (3) any comments by physicians or other professionals involved in long-term care.

The information in the file folders must be accurate and the inspection reports should be current. Nursing home inspections are done by the licensure agency through the entire year, so the new reports will be available sporadically.

In addition to inspection reports, it would be a valuable service if a center would build a resource library. It should have fact sheets, consumer guides, and pamphlets dealing with choosing a nursing home and could also contain various books, articles, government reports, etc., about the nursing home issue and the long term care system. The League recommends an area map be available, marked to show the location of each facility for which information is provided.

It is a good idea to maintain a log of how many people visit the center or telephone for information. The log could also include the kinds of questions that were asked and who asked them: individual consumers, professionals, or representatives of nursing homes, hospitals, or the news media. This information will be helpful later to demonstrate that the center is actively assisting the public, and it might help in an attempt to obtain funding. It can also be used as an evaluation tool to indicate how the information center might be improved.

When the center is ready to open to the general public, the sponsoring group should issue a press release and hold a news conference. In announcing the new information service to the public and the media, the League recommends that emphasis be placed on the following: (1) the service is free to the public; (2) the service offers a centralized file of Medicare/Medicaid inspection reports not available in like form elsewhere; (3) that the information is not evaluative, but simply presents

information that has been collected by the government; and
(4) the center's operating days and hours.

The information center will be valuable not only to potential consumers, but also to hospital personnel and social service
workers who need information on nursing homes. These professionals often have the responsibility for placing patients in
facilities, yet have little more information about the various
homes than the average consumer. Church groups, senior citizen clubs and centers, as well as local health planning bodies
should be notified about the information center.

The League was the first to admit to the program's short-
comings. Obviously, official inspection records are not enough
to assess a nursing home. Mrs. Esther Peterson, the League's
president, commented, "One thing we can't assess from the
records is the humanity of care a nursing home offers." Visitors to the center have been urged to report their own experiences so their comments can be included in the nursing home
files.

Citizens for Better Care
Mr. Chuck Chomet, Executive Director
960 Jefferson Avenue, East
Detroit, Michigan 48207 (313) 963-0513

Citizens for Better Care was formed in 1969 after the City
of Detroit Common Council passed a resolution asking for an
independent watchdog committee to check on local nursing
homes. The resolution resulted from the many inquiries and
problems directed to Councilman Mel Ravitz. Mr. Chuck Chomet, then a student assistant from the University of Michigan
School of Social Work, was instrumental in developing the
resolution. He has worked with CBC since its inception and is
currently the executive director.

CBC incorporated in 1970. Since then CBC's direction has
continued to come from its community board of directors and
the organizational structure has been supported by membership dues. CBC has continually held periodic meetings for its
membership, which is also informed of CBC activities through
a newsletter.

Its consistent strength has undoubtedly come from the in-
tense and dynamic leadership of the director and committed

and forceful board members, such as Ms. Frieda Gorrecht, a nationally known older advocate from the senior center movement who is also associated with the retired workers program of the Detroit United Auto Workers. Two-thirds of the CBC board of directors are senior citizens — several of them influential in other activities for older people. Many of these older persons participate in the CBC speaker's bureau which is designed to encourage membership in the organization.

Other major support has come from private attorneys who have volunteered their time and the Michigan Legal Services Assistance Program of Wayne State University.

From its beginning, CBC strived for and received high visibility from the press, public agencies, and elected representatives. One of the first strategies was seating representatives on important boards such as the state Department of Health Advisory Committee on Nursing Homes and Homes for the Aged, the area comprehensive health planning agency, the state Nursing Homes Administrators' Advisory Council, and the State Commission on Aging.

As early as 1970, the aggressive organization had found its way to Washington, D.C., to the office of Congressman David Pryor, a national advocate of nursing home reform and later, the Governor of Arkansas. Pryor was encouraged by CBC to hold a congressional forum on nursing homes in Detroit in the spring of 1971.

The work of CBC has been enhanced and supported by local newspapers. The *Detroit Free Press*, noted for its bold and progressive articles on consumer issues, including nursing homes, has written about and consulted CBC in numerous articles. In 1974, one columnist characterized CBC as the organization that "has done more for less for old people in desperate need of help and guidance than any other outfit in town . . . ." An editorial described the work of CBC as "a fantastic bargain in human values."

Two major reasons for the continued press support have been CBC's dedication to serious research and fact-finding about nursing home conditions and their persistent challenges of the practices and policies of state agencies and legislative bodies. As Mr. Chomet stated in 1971, "We intend that when we talk about making changes we will do it with intelligence and knowledge. We want to be in a position of knowing more about any situation than anyone and also of avoiding pie-in-the-sky approaches." The activities of CBC since that time seem to embody this philosophy.

The salaried staff has grown from zero to ten. One of the ever-present problems has been to uncover sources of money for CBC operation. Although in its early years it could get by primarily on membership dues, its heightened activities required new sources of revenue. In the beginning, CBC operated out of a closet-size basement room donated by a local church, its first full-time employee a conscientious objector doing alternate service. Since then CBC has been able to use full-time VISTA volunteers and funding sources have included the region's Comprehensive Health Planning Council, area and state Agencies on Aging, the United Auto Workers, churches, the Wayne County Board of Commissioners, Michigan foundations and, most recently, the United Way.

Since 1972, CBC has operated the nursing home ombudsman project in the Detroit area. At first, funding for this project came from the National Council of Senior Citizens, which had received a demonstration grant from HEW. In 1974, CBC received independent one-year funding from the Wayne County-Detroit Area Agency on Aging. This project money has provided staff resources and provisions for training older volunteer ombudsmen.

In 1970, CBC requested records of nursing home deficiencies. The state health department replied that state law prohibited release of such information. In May 1971, CBC and other interested parties filed suit against health department officials, requesting that the public be permitted to inspect nursing home records of licensure inspection visits. In March 1974, the Michigan Court of Appeals ruled that reports must be available to the public. This decision was later appealed to the Michigan Supreme Court by the nursing home industry organization, but the appeal was rejected. In other legal action, CBC gained access to reports on facilities caring for released mental patients.

Early in its program, CBC began a battle to stop the state health department from notifying nursing homes as to the specific date on which licensure inspections were to occur. CBC and the Michigan nursing home ombudsman project were instrumental in getting legislation introduced and finally passed in 1974 that requires unannounced inspections.

CBC has always processed a large volume of consumer complaints. At first, complaints turned over to the state health
department received inadequate and delayed responses; after
constant pressure from CBC, the department of health promulgated regulations that guarantee that any person or consumer group submitting a nursing home complaint will
receive a timely report of the health department's investigation of that complaint.

In August 1973, CBC released a one-hundred-page report
on the living conditions of released mental patients. In 1974,
the governor's office released its own report which substantiated many of the abuses cited by CBC. In October 1973
the group conducted an orientation session and nursing home
tours for state legislators. In 1974, the Comprehensive Health
Planning Council of Southeast Michigan awarded CBC a contract to prepare background papers on the status of released
mental patients and the impact local zoning laws have on
community placement. In this issue CBC led the struggle, and
state licensing rules for after care homes were promulgated.

CBC has worked with Michigan Nurses Association co-
operatively on "Project Inform: Consumer Use of Nursing
Home Information." This work was made possible through a
grant issued by the Michigan Association for Regional Medical
Programs. The project was designed to help consumers make
use of inspection reports prepared by official state and local
agencies as well as the information from the Social Security
Administration and the state department of social services.

In other legal action, CBC filed a conflict of interest suit
with the Michigan State Board of Ethics regarding a state
health department official whose family had financial and
administrative interests in the nursing home field. Because
this official was involved in the regulation of nursing homes,
the board decided in favor of CBC and the official was transferred to another position.

CBC has participated significantly in special training projects directed toward volunteer ombudsmen and nursing home
employees. Its public educational efforts have included the
development of the booklet "How to Choose a Nursing
Home," as we've noted, with the Institute of Gerontology of
the University of Michigan/Wayne State University.

CBC has maintained vigilant watch over the use of taxpayers' dollars by the state and the nursing home industry. In

1974, it managed to exert enough pressure to be appointed the first citizen representative on the special state legislative committee which recommends the amount of reimbursement nursing homes get from the state for patients.

In 1973 CBC filed a class action suit which could eliminate the "retroactive denial" problem in Medicare. This case resulted from a problem investigated by CBC in 1971. An elderly gentleman who had entered a Detroit nursing home after being certified for Medicare nursing home coverage by his hospital physician was informed by Medicare three months later that his stay would not be paid for by that program. He was forced to pay the facility about $2,000. CBC went to court and in late 1973 the Federal District Court ordered that Medicare reimburse the gentleman for his entire payment.

In the spring of 1975, CBC again went to court, this time to prevent the eviction of a nursing home resident. After an initial temporary restraining order CBC succeeded in having the court order the nursing home to keep the resident it was trying to evict because a relative was complaining of poor care.

Because of its long successful history, CBC has become a special model for other groups around the country. Its work has become nationally known and the organization is frequently asked to lead training workshops and provide speakers at special conferences.

Kansans for the Improvement of Nursing Homes
Mrs. Harriet Nehring, Executive Secretary
810 Avalon Road
Lawrence, Kansas 60044 (913) 843-2277

In October 1975 Kansans for the Improvement of Nursing Homes (KINH) was formally organized, but the genesis of this group actually dates several years earlier when Mrs. Raymond (Petey) Cerf began a one-woman crusade to seek community support for improving nursing home conditions.

Mrs. Cerf began her nursing home work in the 1950s when she was approached by a close friend who had volunteered as a "Gray Lady" for the local Red Cross. The friend encouraged Mrs. Cerf to accompany her in organized visits to a local nursing home. As Mrs. Cerf described it, "I wasn't doing anything for anybody but myself, so I decided to go along." That day she began a three-year "quiet" stint, reading to nursing home patients once a week.

Years later in 1966, through her association with the League of Women Voters, Mrs. Cerf became the chairman of a committee to study the Douglas County Welfare Department. Two nurses did a part of the study which focused on nursing homes. They came back with horror stories of one nursing home that she actually couldn't believe — nor forget.

Some time later, she got the opportunity to talk directly to three aides at that facility. She encouraged each to sign affidavits stating the deplorable conditions under which they worked and the patients lived. Each expressed a willingness to testify publicly in order to close the home, which was owned by three local doctors.

An attempt to act through the local health and welfare departments failed. Mrs. Cerf then saw her personal attorney, who advised her to take her documented evidence directly to the state health department. The sordid but solid evidence she had accumulated shocked the director of the licensing bureau into immediate action. A letter was sent out that same day to the primary owner revoking the facility's license. The next day the newspapers reported the notice of closure.

Although the owner expressed outrage and publicly demanded a hearing, he never officially applied for one, and the home was closed. Within three weeks the one hundred patients had been moved to another facility. The closure of the nursing home was the direct result of Mrs. Cerf's lone action as a citizen advocate.

In 1972 Mrs. Cerf was appointed a consumer representative to the Douglas County Comprehensive Health Planning Council. She soon persuaded the council to get involved in nursing home affairs after she received several nursing home complaints. Together with Ms. Jessie Branson, a nurse now active with KINH, she worked in an unsuccessful attempt to get the county to purchase another nursing home facility to ensure beds for Medicaid patients.

At this same time Mrs. Cerf was active in a survey of nursing homes conducted by the League of Women Voters. Her work began to gain the visible and valuable support of her friends and colleagues in the community.

A major campaign, started by Mrs. Cerf and her friends early in 1973, pressed the state to require mandatory pre-employment training of nurse aides. When Mrs. Cerf lobbied this issue before the state legislative committee on public health and welfare, she was accompanied by the director of the local Red Cross and its director of nursing services, the community director of adult education, the director of the Lawrence-Douglas County health department, and the chairman of the League of Women Voters' committee on nursing homes. She and her friends then influenced a local state Republican senator to introduce a bill which would require aide training and to promote a resolution for a special committee to conduct a legislative study concerning certification of adult care home aides. The resolution passed; the aide training bill did not.

In February 1975, Mrs. Cerf and her friends officially began a statewide campaign to form a "Coalition Committee" that would promote the welfare of present and future Kansas nursing home residents. The letter they circulated to various local and state organizations proposed that a new group be formed to lobby for residents of nursing homes and for the public, which supports nursing home care with tax dollars.

In May 1975 Mrs. Cerf and two other members of a temporary steering committee organized and set out for an adventuresome three-day trip around Kansas to enlist support for the coalition. They met with various-sized groups in seven different cities and found their concern was shared by others, who joined with them to discuss issues and offer solutions for nursing home problems.

In a report of its "crusade," the temporary steering committee, which had then grown to six in number, encouraged all their readers to set aside the date of October 11 for an organizational meeting in Wichita. By this time, the group was sufficiently encouraged to use stationery headed "Kansans for Improvement of Nursing Homes" and listing the temporary steering committee.

In July the group initiated formal contact with the director of the Kansas Department of Health and Environment. The letter advised the director, "It is our hope that we can establish a cooperative working relationship with you and your agency and provide what we believe is much needed input from the consumer's side of the nursing home scene. We hope your desires match ours in this respect and that we will always be able to be frank and open on all matters."

Over the summer months, a small group began the task of preparing for the October organizational meeting. One of the group's primary strategies has been to seek information and support from "outside" experts; the October program was planned accordingly, Mary Adelaide Mendelson, the author of *Tender Loving Greed*, was the keynote speaker for their meeting; another stimulant to participants was the luncheon presentation by Chuck Chomet, executive director of Detroit's CBC.

Approximately 150 persons attended the meeting, held at the Wichita State University Campus Activities Center. Based on an advance list of nominees, members of the planning committee were elected from all the congressional districts. Additional persons were elected from the floor.

After the conference, representatives of KINH participated in hearings held by a special legislative committee directed to study nursing home institutions. KINH urged the committee to endorse legislation requiring pre-employment training of aides by the state as already offered by the state department of education through the Kansas area vocational technical schools. Their statement was signed by eighteen members of the newly elected planning committee.

The organizational conference was followed quickly by a committee meeting attended by twenty-three persons. At that meeting the group voted to retain the executive secretary on a part-time basis with a salary in keeping with contributions and membership fees. The group established committees on membership and finance, bylaws, public relations, legislation, and state agency liaison. Notable actions were planned and policies made.

The membership committee decided nonvoting associate memberships would be available to nursing home administrators and owners. To solicit new membership, they planned to develop a brochure for wide distribution and to set up a speakers' bureau. A monthly newsletter was initiated to keep the membership informed.

The bylaws committee planned to seek legal counsel and to explore the process of incorporation. The public relations committee planned a statewide clipping service for nursing home newspaper articles. They discussed the need for clearance of press releases and the need to organize and inform members of press conferences. They planned to develop a background paper on KINH to give to the press.

The state agency liaison committee discussed the need to
acquire and study rules and regulations. They made plans to
obtain representation on a committee formulated to advise
the health department on aide training legislation. Yet another
committee decided to investigate nonlegislative approaches to
the improvement of nursing homes These would include consciousness-raising of community attitudes, support of the
development of alternatives to nursing home care, improving
the attitudes of the medical profession toward good gerontological care, getting the elderly involved, and advocacy of
patients' rights.

In October, a report on Kansas nursing homes was released
by the Kansas attorney general's office. The report focused on
several substandard homes. The nursing home industry rejected the report as an unfair indictment of the state's good
nursing homes. A state health department spokesman con-
tended that "the report does not represent the typical Kansas
nursing home operation nor do we believe that it was intended
in any sense as a blanket indictment of an entire industry."
In response to the report, the department issued an "Action
Plan for the Care of the Elderly in Nursing Homes in Kansas."

KINH responded to the state activities positively but with a
warning to the public, quoted by the *Topeka Daily Capital*,
that "If the Attorney General's report on nursing homes is
interpreted by Kansans to mean Kansas has only six substandard nursing homes, then Kansans are being sadly bam-
boozled." KINH noted that other homes with repeated violations reported by state public health nurses had gone virtually
unnoticed by the state health department.

In December the KINH steering committee met in Topeka
with fifteen members present. An announcement was made
that the request for representation on the health department
advisory committee to develop an aide training course had
been granted. At this meeting the steering committee assumed
the responsibility of functioning as a clearinghouse for information, as a sounding board, a coordinating group, and a communication center. Committee members made a commitment
to attend meetings once a month on Saturdays until the elec-
tion of permanent officers — each meeting to be held in a
different city. KINH had then grown to 101 members with a
mailing list of 500. And, they had acquired a bank balance of
$597 with all bills for their organizing conference paid.

The committee also began its strategy to promote one of its members as a consumer representative in the Mid-America Health Systems Agency, in the new government health planning program that includes nursing homes in its jurisdiction.

By that time several organizations had joined the coalition — the Women's Auxiliary to the Kansas State Medical Society; the Kansas Association of Retarded Citizens; the Joint Legislative Committee of the American Association of Retired Persons/National Retired Teachers Association; the Community Resources Council of Shawnee County-Section on Aging; and the American Organization of Jewish Women of Johnson County.

One of the first tasks of the steering committee as an information clearinghouse was to obtain copies of the inspection reports in their county health departments. They had not met with success by December, so they wrote to the secretary of the department of health outlining the problem: although a state law had gone into effect in July 1975 requiring release of the reports, some county health officers maintained that they had never received information from the state health department regarding the new law. Others, unsure of what information could be released, refused to release any without an interpretation from the health department. KINH asked the department to instruct local health departments on the existence and interpretation of the law immediately. Responding to the argument that no names could be released on the reports, KINH exclaimed, "The section stating that no individuals be named was intended, we feel, to protect the privacy of the residents, not the bad performance of a poor administrator nor the doctor who does not respond when called." Within two weeks, the department had agreed to the request.

In early 1976 KINH obtained the support of two state legislators — one in the house and one in the senate — who introduced legislation which incorporated most of their ideas on pre-employment training and certification of aides.

In January they conducted a workshop for approximately twenty-five persons on lobbying and monitoring nursing homes. A state nurse who had been involved in the state attorney general's nursing home study instructed participants on how to survey nursing homes.

Members of the group met with the state health director and encouraged him to support their proposals for training and certification of aides. They presented a recommendation that citizens throughout the state be officially designated and authorized to inspect nursing homes unannounced.

Although the group had discussed the idea of asking for a meeting with the governor, they put it aside, thinking it would probably take months, if they got in at all. But encouragement from a local supporter convinced Mrs. Cerf and her friends to give it a try and they were granted an appointment within two weeks. In a bold and forthright manner, four members of the coalition met with the governor in February 1976 to present their rationale for supporting legislation that would require pre-employment training of nurse aides.

Another bold move, noted earlier, was taken by KINH when its executive secretary, Mrs. Harriet Nehring, registered as a lobbyist for the organization.

Meanwhile, in her usual resolute manner, Mrs. Cerf purchased ten shares of stock from a state corporation that owns a chain of nursing homes (as well as a mobile home company and other diversified businesses). Her goal was to "legally and morally, as a stockholder, object to making money out of the skin of patients." Her act of defiance resulted from personal anger at a "disgraceful" local nursing home owned and controlled by the corporation.

As Mrs. Cerf puts it, all they need to act is a "little encouragement." KINH has been encouraged and has taken off like a rocket — one that has been carefully designed and fueled.

Citizens Monitoring Team
For organizational information, contact:
Ms. Patricia Powers
Utah State University
Department of Social Work
Logan, Utah 84322

The Citizens Monitoring Team of Davenport, Iowa, a volunteer-staffed, one-year demonstration project, began in the fall of 1973. The identification and documentation of nursing and boarding home problems spurred local college students, faculty, community members, and elected city officials into action that involved the larger community in improving conditions by visiting facilities and supplementing the inspections made by the public health department. This public involvement in the quality of care bolstered the efforts of the regulatory agencies and was a catalyst in moving the responsible agencies and organizations to act more forcefully and creatively on behalf of Iowa's infirm.

The CMT concept first emerged when Marycrest College social welfare and nursing students reported horror stories about the generally wretched conditions of the city's care homes to an atypical college faculty member, Ms. Patricia Powers of the Marycrest social welfare department. Ms. Powers had just moved to Davenport from Washington, D.C., where she had directed several of Ralph Nader's Public Citizen projects, and her experience in public interest and advocacy work moved students and the community into action.

A small number of students, faculty, and community representatives first explored various concerns and strategies. A public watchdog group, they decided, was needed to monitor nursing homes to assure that residents were protected, that their needs were being met and that the facilities were complying with the new state rules and regulations. The second need was for the responsible involvement of city officials, specifically the mayor's office. Davenport's city charter, the group learned, authorized the mayor to "intervene, protect and recommend any measure to improve the health, security and comfort of its citizens." Thus the mayor had a legal obligation to assure that older people in the city's nursing homes were protected. The city charter also specifically stated that the mayor had a legal obligation to assure that nursing homes were fire-safe; the mayor signed applications for nursing home licenses based on compliance with fire safety regulations.

The citizen group argued that unless the mayor had a committee of citizens to visit facilities and ascertain information about compliance with rules and regulations, fire drills, emergency plans, personnel on duty, etc., the mayor was licensing homes in a routine manner. The group told city officials that if a fire did occur, they would be accused of fulfilling their obligations in a perfunctory way and would be held accountable for not taking fire inspection and licensing responsibilities more seriously.

The need for bipartisan support for the CMT concept was obvious. Since city elections were upcoming, both mayoralty candidates were invited to visit local facilities with the citizen

group. The incumbent, Kathryn Kirschbaum, accepted the
offer and later was quoted by the news media as stating she
had "found conditions unfit for human beings." The other
candidate declined the offer as he was "too busy with the
campaign."

Nursing home conditions had become a political campaign
issue and the group took advantage of a political forum held at
the college to ask both candidates if they would support the
concept and implementation of a citizens monitoring team.
Both readily agreed that they would lend their support and
auspices.

Shortly after her re-election, Mayor Kirschbaum called upon
the group to submit a proposal and plan for implementation of
the CMT. A scurry of planning, organizing, and writing activity
took place. The resulting four-page proposal described the
functions and responsibilities of the monitoring team. Its purpose, in the formal language of the proposal, was to ". . . act as
a supplement to the inspector and inspections made by the
state public health department, with the purpose of visiting
Davenport's nursing, boarding, custodial and extended care
homes to encourage compliance with state rules and regulations, and if necessary, to offer appropriate assistance and
recommendations in attempting to facilitate compliance."

The CMT planned to use three approaches to its tasks:
visiting care homes; providing help to facilities; and acting as a
consumer advocate. The intention was not to be a substitute
for the official regulatory agencies nor to discredit every care
home in the city, but to move in positive ways to address community concerns.

In February 1974, the mayor formally accepted the proposal, stating that an important concept was the plan to provide the organization of direct help to the facilities. The CMT
attempted to help the administrators and owners develop
quality care programs for residents; recruit volunteers; expand
social service, recreation, and socialization programs. Another
attractive part of the proposal was that it was a voluntary program with no anticipated costs to the city.

As one might expect, the reaction to these first steps of the
program's implementation was not cause for celebration for
all. The citizen group appeared to have scored a victory, but
the nursing home industry and some government officials expressed criticism, hostility, fear, and uncertainty. Suddenly

the mayor's office turned into a stomping ground for nursing home administrators, owners, their attorneys, and city, county, and state officials, all trying to persuade the mayor that the CMT really wasn't needed. Local health and welfare agencies were also dubious about the program and questioned the autonomy of the monitoring team. Several members of the county board of supervisors publicly attacked the concept and the mayor for lending her auspices to the CMT. At the same time the CMT group began asking civic organizations, unions, churches, and private citizens to write and call the mayor offering support for her efforts in appointing the citizens' committee. In the middle of this chaos, the mayor told the project coordinator, "You know, we really must be on to something, or why else would there be all this commotion?"

The mayor's acceptance of the CMT proposal carried no authority for CMT inspection of each facility; the program was to be completely voluntary and based on cooperative action, which meant, of course, that administrators had the right to refuse the CMT admittance. In a letter sent to administrators and owners, announcing the purpose and functions of the CMT, the mayor urged them to cooperate, especially in light of her responsibilities to sign the fire safety licenses. The reaction was a mixture of acceptance, cooperation, frustration, suspicion, and rejection. Equal numbers of facilities agreed to participate, refused to participate, and were uncertain and wanted a special meeting.

Two meetings were held and administrators told the mayor and project coordinator that more inspections were not needed, that they were already complying with the rules and regulations so "why pick on us?" There was, however, general agreement about a suspected "double standard" in the inspection and licensing process. While some facilities were required to comply with regulations, others had been issued a full license without apparent full compliance, and some of these had major problems. Administrators had little response when the project coordinator asked why they had not been able to "clean their own house"; perhaps the community was needed to help ensure that all homes provided adequate and safe care. All but one of the administrators attending the meeting agreed to cooperate and participate in the program.

Actual CMT membership was to be based on predetermined criteria and ten individuals were selected, agreed to serve, and were formally appointed by the mayor. The committee consisted of individuals with various kinds of expertise and included representatives of the community, older people, and the fields of nursing, social welfare, and nutrition. Orientation and training were provided to all team members. The auspices of the mayor's office were advantageous because the CMT was able to function somewhat independently with no allegiance to any agency, board, or planning body, not even to a politically appointed task force.

To ward off possible criticism, the inspection of facilities had to be as objective as possible. The group decided to use the same criteria for the inspection process as did the Iowa State Health Department: the state rules and regulations for health care facilities. The Iowa Code consisted of ten chapters, totaling 115 pages of regulations; using it was an awesome task for any inspector, especially the volunteer CMT members. A comprehensive, yet workable, evaluation tool was devised by categorizing the regulations to correspond with the areas of expertise of the CMT members. Inspection checklists were prepared by stating each regulation in the form of a question and a corresponding audit sheet was developed for the documentation of findings.

Three- to four-member teams were formed and each was given a list of facilities which it was to monitor. Each facility was visited at least twice, more often if conditions were poor and patient safety was questioned. The first visit was announced and the team met with the administrator or owner to determine current status, problems, and whether community assistance was needed in meeting the stringent new rules and regulations. The second, unannounced visits were usually conducted during mealtime and the team spent this time talking to residents or staff rather than checking the compliance status of technical and physical plant regulations.

Inspection reports written following each visit listed each violation and the suggested plan of correction. The facilities' strengths and positive aspects of the patient care were also documented. The reports were available for public review at the mayor's office and were forwarded to the county and state public health and social service departments, the fire marshal, and the individual facility. After the county and state regulatory agencies began to receive the CMT reports regularly, the criticism from the local health and welfare agency officials stopped. In fact, it was the inspection reports which heightened the group's credibility, because they were so "professional."

The service function of the CMT was turned over to Churches United, a coalition of area churches. When the CMT or the individual facility identified a need or requested community support and involvement, the church group was prepared to provide the requested services. Volunteers, friendly visitors, transportation, etc. were solicited and organized.

The advocacy functions of the CMT were heightened and came to public attention when the area health planning council was considering a specific nursing home proposal. As a new source of community information, the CMT played a major role in the defeat of a new "human warehouse" in Davenport.

The corporation submitting the proposal for the 306-bed facility had the reputation of owning the "worst" facilities in the surrounding three-county area. Organizing and working with other community groups, the CMT submitted critiques, statements, testimony and attended review board hearings at the local and state level.

The major controversy concerned the past performance of the applicant and the greatly diverse mix of patients. The CMT was not allowed to visit the facilities owned by this corporation, but it was a student's visit to one of these facilities in the fall of 1973 that had really initiated the CMT concept. The proposal before the health planning council called for the admittance of not only the elderly, but also drug abuse patients, juvenile and adult criminals, the mentally retarded and mentally ill, and alcoholics. In other words, a planned warehouse for society's unwanted. In fact, the community needed three hundred boarding home beds, but the proposal called for three hundred basic nursing home beds — the Medicaid reimbursement rate of course was higher for the basic than the boarding home beds.

In August 1974, the CMT completed its inspection functions and submitted a formal report of its findings and recommendations to the mayor and to the community.

Definite improvements in conditions did occur as a result of the CMT. The cooperation from most facilities was encouraging. Even those homes which team members were not allowed to visit were later reported to have made improvements in response to the increased expectations and demands of the community.

The CMT had acted decisively when serious problems arose affecting the immediate safety and well-being of residents. Such cases, however, were the exception not the rule. Far more homes were found to be giving adequate care than inadequate care. The more common problems were the lack of activities and rehabilitation programs, the rapid turnover of staff, and the shortage of both professional and ancillary staff.

A major recommendation in the form of a proposed city ordinance would have authorized strict investigation and inspection procedures prior to the issuance of boarding home licenses. Even though this recommendation was not implemented, boarding homes received closer public and agency scrutiny.

Other recommendations were readily accepted and implemented. The mayor's office provided public access to the CMT inspection reports. The CMT prepared and the mayor published a simple directory of community nursing and boarding homes. As the sample page in Chapter Nine shows, the directory contained a subjective evaluation and description as well as the past and present licensing status, information not previously readily available to the public.

As a new experimental project, the efforts of the CMT captured the interest of federal, state, and local agencies and organizations. A letter from the Senate Special Committee on Aging, for example, commended Mayor Kirschbaum and the members of the CMT. The CMT also received much television and newspaper publicity.

The fact that the entire project was developed, organized, and implemented on a volunteer basis, is indeed commendable, impressive, and perhaps incredible. The cost to the city was almost nonexistent. The only expenses were the secretarial, duplication, and mailing costs involved in sending out the inspection reports. Without a full-time paid staff member to coordinate the volunteer services, however, the CMT was unable to provide as much immediate practical help to facilities as they would have liked.

Many citizens have to be encouraged to vote, let alone help oversee our nation's regulatory agencies. The idea of a CMT fulfills two functions simultaneously: protection of those

citizens who cannot defend themselves and the development
of citizens who are willing to serve the public's interest.

National Citizens Coalition for Nursing Home Reform
Contact: Ms. Elma Griesel
National Paralegal Institute
2000 P Street NW
Washington, D.C. 20036 (202) 872-0755
or: Mr. Chuck Chomet
Citizens for Better Care
960 Jefferson Avenue, East
Detroit, Michigan 48207 (313) 963-0513

On June 11, 1975, fifteen consumer organizations from ten
states announced the formation of the National Citizens Coalition for Nursing Home Reform. The coalition meeting pre-
ceded a two day conference entitled "Participative Management in Nursing Homes," sponsored by the American Health
Care Association and George Washington University. The
conference was designed to bring together nursing home
owners, administrators, health care professionals, consumers,
and government representatives to explore solutions to nursing
home problems. The National Gray Panthers had called the
advance meeting of the consumer/action groups so that they
could get to know one another and join together in developing a reform platform to present to the conference in a united
consumer voice. On the opening day of the conference the
coalition held a press conference announcing its formation and
proposed several recommendations for reform. On the closing
day of the conference the coalition presented a summary
report to the participants. It is hoped that the coalition can
provide the vehicle through which consumer groups can keep
informed of current movements for change and, when necessary, present their views in a solid consumer bloc. The coalition can be forceful leverage at the national level to counter-
act the powerful weight that the industry associations have
with government regulatory agencies and elected officials.

Long-Term Care Resource Materials

U.S. Senate Special Committee on Aging Resource Materials

Nursing Home Care in the United States: Failure in Public Policy. U.S. Senate Special Committee on Aging, Subcommittee on Long-Term Care. Order from Government Printing Office, Washington, D.C. 20402. (For some of the subcommittee's findings, see our Appendix B.

"Introductory Report," report no. 93-1420, November 1974. Stock no. 5270-02621; $1.85.

Supporting Paper No. 1, "The Litany of Nursing Home Abuses and an Examination of the Roots of Controversy," December 1974. Stock no. 5270-02650; $1.20.

Supporting Paper No. 2, "Drugs in Nursing Homes: Misuse, High Costs, and Kickbacks," January 1975. $1.20.

Supporting Paper No. 3, "Doctors in Nursing Homes: The Shunned Responsibility," February 1975. Stock no. 052-070-02757; $.80.

Supporting Paper No. 4, "Nurses in Nursing Homes: The Heavy Burden," April 1975. $1.50.

Supporting Paper No. 5, "The Continuing Chronicle of Nursing Home Fires," August 1975; $1.65

Supporting Paper No. 6, "What Can be Done in Nursing Homes: Positive Aspects in Long-Term Care," September 1975. Stock no. 052-070-03084-4; $1.70.

Supporting Paper No. 7, "The Role of Nursing Homes in Caring for Discharged Mental Patients," March 1976. $1.60.

Supporting Paper No. 8. "Access to Nursing Homes by U.S. Minorities."

Supporting Paper No. 9, "Profits and the Nursing Home: Incentives in Favor of Poor Care."

Two final documents will be issued as part of this study: a compendium of statements by national organizations and administration spokesmen, and a final report by the Subcommittee on Long-Term Care. Information on release dates and prices not given can be obtained from the Senate Committee on Aging.

Other important materials available from the committee include:

Development in Aging: Part 1 and Part 2, 1975 and January-May 1976. A report of the Special Committee on Aging. Report no. 94-998.

Developments in Aging: 1974 and January-April 1975. A report of the Special Committee on Aging. Report no. 94-250.

Developments in Aging: 1973 and January-March 1974. A report of the Special Committee on Aging. Report no. 93-846.

Developments in Aging: 1972 and January-March 1973. A report of the Special Committee on Aging. Stock no. 5271-00346; $1.75.

Memorandum. A periodic newsletter report prepared by the Special Committee on Aging. There is no charge to be placed on the mailing list to receive the *Memorandum.*

General Information

Butler, Robert N., M.D., *Why Survive? Being Old in America* (New York: Harper & Row, 1975).

Downey, Gregg W., "AHCA Conference: Where the 'Monster' Met the People," *Modern Health Care,* Aug. 1975, p. 11.

Garvin, Richard, and Robert Burger, *Where They Go to Die: The Tragedy of America's Aged* (New York: Delacorte, 1968).

Mendelson, Mary Adelaide, *Tender Loving Greed* (New York: Knopf, 1974).

Modern Health Care, a McGraw-Hill magazine, incorporating *Modern Nursing Home* Excellent articles on nursing home issues and special reporting on current events in the nursing home field. Subscription $17.00; 230 W. Monroe St., Chicago, Ill. 60606.

Tulloch, G. Janet, *A Home Is Not a Home (Life Within a Nursing Home)* (New York: Seabury Press, 1976).

Choosing a Nursing Home

American Health Care Association, "Thinking About a Nursing Home?" AHCA, 1200 15th Street, N.W., Washington, D.C. 20005. Free.

Citizens for Better Care and The Institute of Gerontology, University of Michigan/Wayne State University, *How to Choose a Nursing Home: A Shopping and Rating Guide.* 543 Church St., Ann Arbor, Mich. 48104; $1.00.

"How to Choose a Nursing Home," *Changing Times,* Jan. 17, 1974, pp. 35-39.

U.S. Department of Health, Education and Welfare, *Nursing Home Care: Consumer Information on the Selection of a Nursing Home.* Stock no. 1761-00032; $.40.

Alternatives to Nursing Homes

Ketcham, William; Ann Sack; and Herbert Shore: "Annotated Bibliography on Alternatives to Institutional Care," *The Gerontologist*, Feb. 1974, pp. 34-36.
Pima Council on Aging, *A Plan of Long Term Care Services for Pima County: A Continuum of Care* (Tucson, Ariz.: Pima Council on Aging, July 1975). Suite 406, 100 E. Alameda St., Tucson, Ariz. 85701.
U. S., Senate, Special Committee on Aging, *Alternatives to Nursing Home Care: A Proposal*, 1971. Stock no. 5270-1248; $.20.
———, *Congregate Housing for Older Adults: Assisted Residential Living Combining Shelter and Services: A Working Paper*, Nov. 1975.
———, *Home Health Services in the United States*, prepared by Brahna Trager, 1972. $1.30.
———, *Home Health Services in the United States: A Working Paper on Current Status*, July 1973. Stock no. 5270-01874; $.50.
University of South Carolina, Social Problems Research Institute, *Alternatives to Institutional Care for the Elderly in South Carolina*, prepared for the South Carolina Commission on Aging, Aug. 1974.

Organizing Resources

Ross, Donald, *A Public Citizen's Action Manual* (New York: Grossman, 1973).
O.M. Collective, The, *The Organizer's Manual* (New York: Bantam, 1971).
Midwest Academy, "Direct Action Organizing: A Handbook for Women," 1973. 600 W. Fullerton, Chicago, Ill. 60614; mimeographed; $1.75
Source Collective, *Organizing for Health Care: A Tool for Change: Source Catalog 3* (Boston: Beacon Press, 1974). $5.95.

Public Interest Research Group Investigations and Reports

Conn PIRG Reports, *The Nursing Home*, Sept. 1974. Connecticut PIRG, P.O. Box 1571, Hartford, Conn. 06101; $1.00.

ISPIRG Reports, *Report on Iowa's Nursing Homes and Related Care Facilities*, Dec. 1974. Iowa Student PIRG, 104 E. Jefferson, Iowa City, Iowa 52240; $2.00.

Maine PIRG Reports, *Would You Call This Home? Maine Nursing Homes: A Consumer's Perspective*, Nov. 1974. Maine PIRG, 2 Stone St., Augusta, Me. 04330.

OSPIRG Reports, *Nursing Home Patients: Who Protects Them?* June 1974. An in-depth study of Oregon nursing homes. Oregon Student PIRG, 411 Governor Bldg., 408 S.W. Second Ave., Portland, Ore. 97204.

Townsend, Claire, and Ralph Nader's Study Group Report on Nursing Homes, *Old Age: The Last Segregation* (New York: Bantam, 1971).

Citizens' Groups Reports and Manuals

The Action Coalition of Elders, *Kane Hospital: A Place to Die*, Oct. 1975. P.O. Box 7587, Pittsburgh, Pa. 15213.

The American Jewish Congress, *The Last Resort: A Citizen's Guide to Nursing Home Reform*, July 1974. 15 East 84th St., New York, N.Y. 10028.

Horn, Linda L., *Community Care: A Citizens Monitoring Team Report of Davenport's Health Care Facilities*, Aug. 1974. Available from Patricia Powers, Utah State Univ., Dept. of Sociology and Social Work, Logan, Utah 84322; $5.00.

Mid-Coast Comprehensive Health Planning Association, in cooperation with Citizens for Better Nursing Home Care, *Nursing Homes and Alternative Care: A Consumer's Guide*, Jan. 1976. P.O. Box 1068, Salinas, Cal. 93901; $1.00.

National Consumers League, "How to Set up a Health Service Information Center," 1974. 1785 Massachusetts Ave., N.W., Washington, D.C. 20036; mimeographed, $3.00.

State and Local Government Reports

Los Angeles, Office of the City Attorney, *Nursing Home Hearing Examiner's Report*, March 1975, and *Los Angeles Nurs-*

ing Homes: A Report and Recommendations for New Programs to Benefit Nursing Home Patients, prepared by Burt Pines, city attorney; Aileen Adams, project coordinator; Max Factor, hearing examiner.

Maryland, Governor's Commission on Nursing Homes, *The Government, the Community, the Institutions*, July 1973.

New York State, Moreland Act Commission, *Regulating Nursing Home Care: The Paper Tigers*, Oct. 1975, and *Reimbursement of Nursing Home Property Costs: Pruning the Money Tree*, Jan. 1976. 270 Broadway, New York, N.Y. 10017.

Pennsylvania, House, Health and Welfare Committee, "The Nursing Home Problem in Pennsylvania: An Opportunity to Serve," Sept. 1974, and "The Nursing Home Problem in Pennsylvania: Financing Quality Care," Feb. 1976.

Travis County (Texas) Committee on Aging, Adult Services Council, "An Inquiry into Some Problem Areas in Nursing Homes in Travis County," Feb. 1975. 1005 W. Sixth St., Austin, Tex. 78703.

Federal Government Reports

U.S., Department of Health, Education, and Welfare, Administration on Aging, Office of Human Development, *Ombudsman for Nursing Homes: Structure and Process*, 1975. Order from the Administration on Aging.

——, Public Health Service, Office of Nursing Home Affairs, "Interpretive Guidelines and Survey Procedures for Skilled Nursing Facilities and Intermediate Care Facilities," Mar. 1975 with revisions. Order from Office of Nursing Home Affairs.

——, *Long-Term Care Facility Improvement Study: Introductory Report*, July 1975. Order from Office of Nursing Home Affairs; DHEW Publication No. (OS) 76-50021.

——, *1974 Regulations for Skilled Nursing Facilities and Intermediate Care Facilities: Chart Booklet.* A brief overview of the legislative and administrative history surrounding long-term care under Medicare and Medicaid to explain a facet of governmental involvement in standard setting for long-term care. Order from Office of Nursing Home Affairs.

Patients' Rights

Federation of Protestant Welfare Agencies, Division on Aging, *Establishing Resident Councils: Guidelines for Residents and Administrators.* 281 Park Ave., New York, N.Y. 10010; $0.50.

Ferleger, David, "A Patients' Rights Organization: Advocacy and Collective Action by and for Inmates of Mental Institutions," *Clearinghouse Review,* Jan. 1975. National Clearinghouse for Legal Service, 710 N. Lake Shore Dr., Chicago, Ill. 60611.

Medical Committee for Human Rights, "Patients' Rights and Advocacy." P.O. Box 7155, Pittsburgh, Pa. 15213.

New York Health Facilities Association, Inc., "Patients' Rights and Public Accountability," July 16, 1975. 203 Loew Bldg., Syracuse, N.Y. 13202.

Steele, Mark M., "A Voice for Nursing Home Residents," *Modern Health Care,* Feb. 1976. p. 13.

University of Pennsylvania Health Law Project, "Legal Problems Inherent in Organizing Nursing Home Occupants," *Clearinghouse Review,* Aug.-Sept. 1972, pp. 203-211. National Clearinghouse for Legal Services, 710 N. Lake Shore Dr., Chicago, Ill. 60611.

———, "Patients' Right: What Are They: The Law and Nursing Homes." 133 S. 36th St., Philadelphia, Pa. 19104.

Legal Resources

Brown, Robert N., "An Appraisal of the Nursing Home Enforcement Process," *Arizona Law Review,* 17, 2 (1975). For single copy: Fred B. Rothman & Company, 57 Leuning St., South Hackensack, N.J. 07606; $3.00.

The Nursing Home Law Letter, published monthly by the National Senior Citizens Law Center; first issue Jan. 1976.

Regan, John J., "Quality Assurance Systems in Nursing Homes," *Journal of Urban Law,* 53, 2 (Fall 1975).

Wilson, Sally Hart, *The Nursing Home Law Manual* (Los Angeles: National Senior Citizens Law Center, 1975); $1.50.

Western Center on Law and Poverty, "How to Represent Patients of Skilled Facilities at Fair Hearings." 1709 West 8th St., Suite 600, Los Angeles, Calif. 90017.

Government Information

Department of Health, Education, and Welfare (HEW)

General Information Directory (202) 245-6296

Assistant Secretary for Health	Special Assistant
Dr. Theodore Cooper	HEW Undersecretary
Room 5077,	Mr. Peter Franklin
HEW North Building	Room 5651
330 Independence Avenue, S.W.	HEW North Building
Washington, D.C. 20201	(same address)
(202) 245-7694	(202) 245-7591

OFFICE OF NURSING HOME AFFAIRS (ONHA)

Dr. Faye Abdellah, Director
5600 Fishers Lane, Room 17B-07
Rockville, Maryland 20852
(301) 443-6497
   Charged with coordinating long-term care enforcement programs of the SRS, MSA, SSA, and the Mental Health Administration. It is also responsible for policy development. In December 1974, ONHA signed an agreement with AoA which extended its responsibilities to include the coordination of all HEW health care programs for older people.

HEALTH SERVICES ADMINISTRATION (HSA)

Michael Goran, M.D., Director
Bureau of Quality Assurance
5600 Fishers Lane, Room 16A-55
Rockville, Maryland 20852
(301) 443-3880
   Concerned with the cost, quality, and utilization of health care services provided by Medicare, Medicaid, and other federal programs.

HEALTH RESOURCES ADMINISTRATION (HRA)

Bureau of Health Services Research
Division of Long-Term Care
5600 Fishers Lane, Room 11A-33
Rockville, Maryland 20852
(301) 443-1376

Concerned with the requirements for and the distribution of health resources, including manpower training such as nurse aide training.

SOCIAL AND REHABILITATION SERVICE (SRS)

Medical Services Administration (MSA)
330 C Street, S.W.
Washington, D.C. 20201
Administers the federal Medicaid program.

SOCIAL SECURITY ADMINISTRATION

Bureau of Health Insurance
6401 Security Boulevard
Baltimore, Maryland 21235
(301) 594-9000
Provides direction for the administration of the Medicare Program. Develops and modifies conditions of participation and principles for reimbursing providers of health services.

(Bureau of Supplemental Security
Income for the Aged, Blind, and
Disabled)
Administers the SSI program.

ADMINISTRATION ON AGING (AoA)

Arthur S. Flemming, Commissioner
400 6th Street, S.W., Room 4030
Washington, D.C. 20201
(202) 245-0724
Administers programs established by the Older Americans Act, including model project grants to develop state ombudsman programs.

Nursing Home Interests Staff
Cenoria Johnson, Director
and Sue Bailey Wheaton
Room 3121
(202) 245-6810

NURSING HOME OMBUDSMAN PROGRAMS

The programs listed below were originally funded as three-year demonstration projects by HEW. Their experiences and written reports may be of value to you in your work. Addresses for all state Ombudsman Development Specialists employed in 1975-76 can be obtained from the AoA Nursing Home Interests Staff.

Carol A. Delaney, Director
Pennsylvania Nursing Home
  Ombudsman Project
133 South 36th Street,
Room 501
Philadelphia, Pennsylvania
19104
(215) 238-7776

William V. Bradley, Director
Nursing Home Ombudsman
  Program
915 South Main Street
Columbia, South Carolina
29201
(803) 758-2576

Lawrence Fish, Director
Upper Peninsula Nursing
  Home Ombudsman Project
107 10th Avenue
Menominee, Michigan 49858
(906) 864-2385

Douglas Roberts, Director
Ombudsman Project
Citizens for Better Care
960 Jefferson Avenue, East
Detroit, Michigan 48207
(313) 568-0526

Arlene Warner, Director
Nursing Home Ombudsman
  Program
Idaho Office on Aging
506 North 5th Street
Boise, Idaho 83707
(208) 384-3833

J. J. Donovan
State Nursing Home
  Ombudsman
Office of Elder Affairs
120 Boylston Street
Boston, Massachusetts
02116
(617) 727-7275

David J. Krings
Nursing Home Ombudsman
  Program
Office of the Lieutenant
  Governor
201 East Washington Avenue
  Room 498
Madison, Wisconsin 53702
(608) 266-8944

OFFICE OF LONG-TERM CARE STANDARDS ENFORCEMENT

**Regional Directors and
Long-Term Care Education Coordinators**

Region, Names, and Addresses   *Telephone Numbers*

Region I
Thomas Sullivan, Director   (617) 223-3698

John Fitzgerald Kennedy Building
Government Center
Boston, Massachusetts 02203

Richard W. Orzechowski   (617) 223-5495
Long-Term Care Education Coordinator

(Region I includes Connecticut, Massachusetts, Maine, New
Hampshire, Vermont, and Rhode Island)

Region II
Al Saperstein, Director   (212) 264-3496
Federal Building
26 Federal Plaza
New York, New York 10007

Douglas A. Mahy   (212) 264-3496
Long-Term Care Education Coordinator

(Region II includes New York, New Jersey, Puerto Rico, and
Virgin Islands)

Region III
Robert J. Taylor, Director   (215) 597-6550
3535 Market Street
P.O. Box 13716
Philadelphia, Pennsylvania 19101

Pauline Jones   (215) 597-6556
Long-Term Care Education Coordinator

(Region III includes Delaware, District of Columbia, Maryland,
Pennsylvania, Virginia, and West Virginia)

Region IV
John Pipes, Director   (404) 526-5338
Peachtree-Seventh Building
50 Seventh Street, N.E.
Atlanta, Georgia 30323

Isom H. Herron, III   (404) 526-3636
Long-Term Care Education Coordinator

(Region IV includes Alabama, Florida, Georgia, Kentucky,
Mississippi, North Carolina, South Carolina, and Tennessee)

Region V
Marvin Hitt, Director   (312) 353-8856
300 South Wacker Drive
Chicago, Illinois 60607

Walter Hedrick   (312) 353-8857
Long-Term Care Education Coordinator

(Region V includes Illinois, Indiana, Minnesota, Michigan,
Ohio, and Wisconsin)

Region VI
Mary Lou Lane, Director   (214) 729-3546
1114 Commerce Street
Dallas, Texas 75202

Meral Loewus, R.N.   (214) 749-3381
Long-Term Care Education Coordinator

(Region VI includes Arkansas, Louisiana, New Mexico, Okla-
homa, and Texas)

Region VII
David E. Watson, Director   (816) 374-3436
Federal Office Building
601 East 12th Street
Kansas City, Missouri 64106

Arthur Forest   (816) 374-5104
Long-Term Care Education Coordinator

(Region VII includes Iowa, Kansas, Missouri, and Nebraska)

Region VIII
Al Buckingham, Director   (303) 837-4861
19th and Stout Streets
Denver, Colorado 80202

John Allis   (303) 837-4861
Long-Term Care Education Coordinator

(Region VIII includes Colorado, Montana, North Dakota,
South Dakota, Utah, and Wyoming)

Region IX
Harold Coleman, Director   (415) 556-5342
Federal Office Building
50 Fulton Street
San Francisco, California 94102

Dr. Hugh F. Sloan   (415) 556-5342
Long-Term Care Education Coordinator

(Region IX includes Arizona, California, Nevada, Hawaii,
Guam, American Samoa, and the Trust Territories of the
Pacific Islands)

Region X
Donald Jaques, Director   (206) 442-7222
Arcade Plaza Building
1321 Second Avenue
Seattle, Washington 98101

Don Williams   (206) 442-7222
Long-Term Care Education Coordinator

(Region X includes Alaska, Idaho, Oregon, and Washington)

Note: Regional Long-Term Care Education Centers have been
established for the purpose of training multidisciplinary teams
from long-term care facilities to improve the quality of care
delivered by providers. Ask your Long-Term Care Education
Coordinator about the location of the center in your area and
the programs it offers. Request participation in the program as
appropriate.

Legislative Resources

U. S. SENATE SPECIAL COMMITTEE ON AGING

Senator Frank Church, Chairman
Dirksen Senate Office Building, Room G-225
Washington, D.C. 20510
(202) 224-5364

SUBCOMMITTEE ON LONG-TERM CARE

Senator Frank Moss, Chairman
Val Halamandaris, Associate Counsel

U. S. HOUSE OF REPRESENTATIVES SELECT
COMMITTEE ON AGING

Representative William J. Randall, Chairman
Subcommittee on Health and Long-Term Care
712 House Office Building, Annex #1
Washington, D.C. 20515
(202) 225-9375

Other Special Resources

American Jewish Congress
  Women's Division Nursing
  Home Program
15 East 84th Street
New York, New York 10028

Medical Committee for
  Human Rights
P. O. Box 7155
Pittsburgh, Pennsylvania
15213

Federation for Community
  Planning
Health Planning and Develop-
  ment Commission
Mildred Barry, Director
1001 Huron Road
Cleveland, Ohio 44115
(216) 781-2944

National Senior Citizens
  Law Center
Paul Nathanson, Director
Sally Hart Wilson, Nursing
  Home Specialist
1709 West 8th Street
Los Angeles, California 90017
(213) 483-3990

National Council of
  Senior Citizens
Legal Research and Services
  for the Elderly
David Marlin, Director
1511 K Street, N.W.
Washington, D.C. 20024
(202) 638-4351

Nursing Home Industry Associations

American Health Care
  Association
(formerly American Nursing
  Home Association)
1200 15th Street, N.W.
Washington, D.C. 20005
(202) 833-2030

American Association of
  Homes for the Aging
374 National Press Building
529 14th Street, N.W.
Washington, D.C. 20004
(202) 347-2000

National Council of Health
  Care Services
Suite 402
1200 15th Street, N.W.
Washington, D.C. 20005
(202) 785-4754

Professional Associations

National Association of
  Social Workers
Suite 600
1425 H Street, N.W.
Washington, D.C. 20005

National League for Nursing
10 Columbus Circle
New York, New York 10019

American Nurses Association
2420 Pershing Road
Kansas City, Missouri 64108

American Medical
  Association
535 North Dearborn Street
Chicago, Illinois 60610

American College of Nursing
  Home Administrators
Suite 409
8641 Colesville Road
Silver Springs, Maryland
20910

American Public Health
  Association
1015 18th Street, N.W.
Washington, D.C. 20036

APPENDIX A

RESIDENT RIGHTS: Intermediate Care Facility Services

[Part 249, Chapter II, Title 45, Code of Federal Regulations, Department of Health, Education and Welfare, Social Security Administration, as printed in the *Federal Register*, 41, 61 (Monday, March 29, 1976) pp. 12883-12885. From §249.12 (a)(1): Standards for intermediate care facilities.]

(ii) There are written policies and procedures available to staff, residents, their families or legal representatives and the public which:

(A) Govern all areas of service provided by the facility:

(1) Admission, transfer, and discharge of residents policies shall assure that:

(i) Only those persons are accepted whose needs can be met by the facility directly or in cooperation with community resources or other providers of care with which it is affiliated or has contracts:

(ii) As changes occur in their physical or mental condition, necessitating service or care which cannot be adequately provided by the facility, residents are transferred promptly to hospitals, skilled nursing facilities, or other appropriate facilities; and

(iii) Except in the case of an emergency, the resident, his next of kin, attending physician, and the responsible agency, if any, are consulted at least five days in advance of the transfer or discharge of any resident, and casework services or other means are utilized to assure that adequate arrangements exist for meeting his needs through other resources.

(2) Policies define the uses of chemical and physical restraints, identify the professional personnel under subparagraph (a)(1)(ii)(B)(7) of this section who may authorize the application of restraints in emergencies and describe the mechanism for monitoring and controlling their use;

(3) Policies define procedures for submittal of complaints and recommendations by residents and for assuring response and disposition; and

(4) There shall be written policies governing access to, duplication of, and dissemination of information from the resident's record;

(B) Ensure that each resident admitted to the facility:

(1) Is fully informed of his rights and responsibilities as a resident and of all rules and regulations governing resident conduct and responsibilities. Such information must be provided prior to or at the time of admission or, in the case of residents already in the facility, upon the facility's adoption or amendment of resident right policies, and its receipt must be acknowledged by the resident in writing; and in the case of a mentally retarded individual, witnessed by a third party;

(2) Is fully informed in writing prior to or at the time of admission and during stay, of services available in the facility, and of related charges including any charges for services not covered under the title XIX program or not covered by the facility's basic per diem rate;

(3) Is fully informed by a physician, of his health and medical condition unless medically contraindicated (as documented by a physician in his resident record), and is afforded the opportunity to participate in the planning of his total care and medical treatment and to refuse treatment, and participates in experimental research only upon his informed written consent;

(4) Is transferred or discharged only for medical reasons or for his welfare or that of other patients, or for nonpayment for his stay (except as prohibited by the title XIX program):

(5) Is encouraged and assisted, throughout his period of stay, to exercise his rights as a resident and as a citizen, and to this end may voice grievances and recommend changes in policies and services to facility staff and/or to outside representatives of his choice, free from restraint, interference, coercion, discrimination, or reprisal;

(6) May manage his personal financial affairs, and to the extent, under written authorization by the resident, that the facility assists in such management, that it is carried out in accordance with paragraph (a)(1)(iii) of this section;

(7) Is free from mental and physical abuse, and free from chemical and physical restraints except as follows: when authorized in writing by a physician for a specified period of time; when necessary in an emergency to protect the resident from injury to himself or to others, in which case restraints may be authorized by designated professional personnel who promptly report the action taken to the physician; and in the case of a

mentally retarded individual when authorized in writing by a physician or Qualified Mental Retardation Professional for use during behavior modification sessions;

(8) In the case of a mentally retarded individual, participates in a behavior modification program involving use of restraints or aversive stimuli only with the informed consent of his parent or guardian;

(9) Is ensured confidential treatment of all information contained in his records, including information contained in an automatic data bank, and his written consent shall be required for the release of information to persons not otherwise authorized under law to receive it;

(10) Is treated with consideration, respect, and full recognition of his dignity and individuality, including privacy in treatment and in care for his personal needs;

(11) Is not required to perform services for the facility;

(12) May communicate, associate and meet privately with persons of his choice, unless to do so would infringe upon the rights of other residents, and send and receive his personal mail unopened;

(13) May participate in activities of social, religious, and community groups at his discretion, unless contraindicated for reasons documented by a Qualified Mental Retardation Professional as appropriate in his resident record;

(14) May retain and use his personal clothing and possessions as space permits; and

(15) If married, is ensured privacy for visits by his/her spouse; if both are residents in the facility, they are permitted to share a room.

(C) Provide that all rights and responsibilities of the resident devolve to the resident's guardian, next of kin, or sponsoring agency(ies), where:

(1) a resident is adjudicated incompetent in accordance with State law; or

(2) his physician or, in the case of a mentally retarded individual, a Qualified Mental Retardation Professional has documented in the resident's record the specific impairment that has rendered the resident incapable of understanding these rights.

Effective Date: The regulations in this section shall be effective June 28, 1976.

Note: Provisions for patient rights in skilled nursing facilities, which are similar to ICF regulations, became effective on December 2, 1974, and are printed in the *Federal Register,* 39, 193 (Thursday, October 3, 1974) pp. 35775-35776.

APPENDIX B

Nursing Home Care in the United States: Failure in Public Policy, "Introductory Report," prepared by the Subcommittee on Long-Term Care of the U.S. Senate Special Committee on Aging. November 1974, report no. 93-1420, pp. 5-11.

Major Findings

Medicaid now pays about 50 percent of the Nation's more than $7.5 billion nursing home bill, and Medicare pays another 3 percent. Thus, about $1 of every $2 in nursing home revenues is publicly financed. . . . There are now more nursing home beds (1.2 million) in the United States today than general and surgical beds (1 million). . . . In 1972, for the first time, Medicaid expenditures for nursing home care exceeded payments for surgical and general hospital: 34 percent as compared to 31 percent. . . . Medicaid is essential for growing numbers of elderly, particularly since Medicare nursing home benefits for a retired couple now amount to $310 a month compared to the average nursing home cost of $600. Medicaid (a welfare program) must be called upon to make up the difference . . . . The growth of the industry has been impressive. Between 1960 and 1970, nursing home facilities increased by 140 percent, beds by 232 percent, and patients by 210 percent, employees by 405 percent, and expenditures for care by 465 percent. Measured from 1960 through 1974, expenditures increased about 1400 percent . . . . Despite the heavy Federal commitment to long-term care, a coherent policy on goals and methods has yet to be shaped. Thousands of seniors go without the care they need. Others are in facilities inappropriate to their needs. Perhaps most unfortunate, institutionalization could have been postponed or prevented for thousands of cur-

rent nursing home residents if viable home health care and supportive services existed. Although such alternative forms of
care may be more desirable from the standpoint of elderly
patients — as well as substantially less expensive — the Department of HEW has given only token support for such programs.

Despite the sizable commitment in Federal funds, HEW has
been reluctant to issue forthright standards to provide patients
with minimum protection. Congress in 1972 mandated the
merger of Medicare and Medicaid standards, with the retention
of the higher standard in every case. Most leading authorities
concluded at subcommittee hearings that the new standards
are so vague as to defy enforcement . . . . There is no direct
Federal enforcement of these and previous Federal standards.
Enforcement is left almost entirely to the States. A few do a
good job, but most do not. In fact, the enforcement system
has been characterized as scandalous, ineffective, and, in some
cases, almost nonexistent. . . . The President's program for
"nursing home reform" has had only minimal effect, since it
was first announced in 1971 and actions in 1974 fall far short
of a serious effort to regulate the industry.

The victims of Federal policy failures have been Americans
who are desperately in need of help. The average age of nursing home patients is 82; 95 percent are over 65 and 70 percent are over 70; only 10 percent are married; almost 50 percent have no direct relationship with a close relative. Most can
expect to be in a nursing home over 2 years. And most will die
in the nursing home. These patients generally have four or
more chronic or crippling disabilities . . . . Most national health
insurance proposals largely ignore the long-term care needs of
older Americans. Immediate action is required by the Congress
and executive branch to improve past policies and programs
which have been piecemeal, inappropriate, illusory and short-
lived.

Supporting Paper No. 1 — "The Litany of Nursing Home
Abuses and an Examination of the Roots of Controversy"

. . Abuses of patients in nursing homes have been well publicized and well documented. And yet they persist, perhaps because of the belief that they are exceptions to the rule. However, subcommittee transcripts are replete with examples of
cruelty, negligence, danger from fires, food poisoning, virulent
infections, lack of human dignity, callousness and unnecessary

regimentation, and kickbacks to nursing home operators from suppliers. . . . Estimates on the number of substandard nursing homes in the United States vary widely, but the overwhelming evidence indicates that a majority of the nursing homes fail to meet standards of acceptability. . . . Nursing home placement often is a bitter confirmation of the fears of a lifetime. Seniors fear change and uncertainty; and loss of liberty and human dignity; they fear poor care and abuse; loss of health and mobility. They also fear exhausting their savings and "going on welfare." To the average older American, nursing homes have become almost synonymous with death and protracted suffering before death.

Supporting Paper No. 2 — "Drugs in Nursing Homes: Misuse, High Costs, and Kickbacks"
. . . According to most studies, the average nursing home patient takes 4.2 different medications each day. However, more recent studies reveal that the average may be seven medications, or perhaps even higher. Prescriptions for nursing home patients typically total $300 per year, more than three times the cost for the noninstitutionalized elderly. In 1972, drugs accounted for 10 percent of all nursing home expenditures — $300 million in all. . . . And yet, the flow of drugs through many of America's 23,000 nursing homes is largely without controls. It is haphazard; it is inefficient; and it does not help the patient desperately dependent upon others for protection when put in a state of semisleep or outright unconsciousness.

Supporting Paper No. 3 — "Doctors in Nursing Homes: The Shunned Responsibility"
. . . Physicians have, to a large degree, shunned the responsibility for personal attention to nursing home patients. One of the reasons for their lack of concern is inadequate training at schools of medicine. Another is the negative attitude toward care of the chronically ill in this Nation. Medical directors are needed in U.S. nursing homes and will be required in HEW regulations effective January 1976. The subcommittee's May 1974 questionnaire to the 101 U.S. schools of medicine indicates a serious lack of emphasis on geriatrics and long-term care. . . Eighty-seven percent of the schools indicated that geriatrics was not now a specialty and that they were not contemplating making it one; 74 percent of the schools had no

program by which students, interns, or residents could fulfill requirements by working in nursing homes; and 53 percent stated they had no contact at all with the elderly in nursing homes.

Supporting Paper No. 4 — "Nurses in Nursing Homes: The Heavy Burden (The Reliance on Untrained and Unlicensed Personnel)"

. . . Of the 815,000 registered nurses in this nation, only 56,235 are found in nursing homes, and much of their time is devoted to administrative duties. From 80 to 90 percent of the care is provided by more than 280,000 aides and orderlies, a few of them well trained, but most literally hired off the streets. Most are grossly overworked and paid at or near the minimum wage. With such working conditions, it is understandable that their turnover rate is 75% a year. . . . One reason for the small number of registered nurses in nursing homes is that present staffing standards are unrealistic. The present Federal standard calls for one registered nurse coverage only on the day shift, seven days a week, regardless of the size of the nursing home. By comparison, Connecticut requires one registered nurse for each 30 patients on the day shift, one for every 45 in the afternoon, and one for each 60 in the evening. A serious national shortage of nurses still persists, despite training programs.

Supporting Paper No. 5 — "The Continuing Chronicle of Nursing Home Fires"

. . . In 1971, there were 4,800 nursing home fires; 38 persons were killed in multiple death fires and some 500 more in single death fires. An estimated $3.5 million loss was directly attributable to nursing home fires. . . . Nursing home patients are especially vulnerable to fires. Many are under sedation or bound with restraints. Physical infirmities and confusion often cause resistance to rescue. . . . There is reason to believe the number of nursing homes failing to meet fire safety standards is actually increasing. . . . In 1971, the General Accounting Office reported that 50% of U.S. nursing homes were deficient in regard to fire safety. A January 1974 study by the U.S. Office of Nursing Home Affairs said that 59% of skilled nursing facilities are certified with deficiencies. HEW spokesmen indicated that in excess of 60% of the intermediate facilities do

not comply with existing standards. The requirements are on
the books, but they are not heeded. Even more dramatically,
the GAO 1974 study indicates that 72% of U.S. nursing homes
have one or more major fire deficiencies.

Supporting Paper No. 6 — "What Can Be Done in Nursing
Homes: Positive Aspects in Long-Term Care"
　　. . . It is unjust to condemn the entire nursing home industry. There are many fine homes in America. A growing number
of administrators are insisting upon positive approaches to therapy and rehabilitation, innovations in physical structure of the
physical plant; employee sensitivity training and co-operative
agreements with local schools of nursing; and even self-govern-
ment and other activities for the patients. . . . "Ombudsmen"
programs have been established by Presidential direction and
are making some headway. In some states, the nursing home
industry has launched an effort to upgrade its facilities by
establishing directories, rating systems, and a "peer review"
mechanism. These efforts offer the prospect of improving
nursing home conditions if conducted in a vigorous and effective manner. In Chicago, nursing homes have a "cool line"
telephone number for relatives, visitors, or patients who have
complaints.

Supporting Paper No. 7 — "The Role of Nursing Homes in
Caring for Discharged Mental Patients"
　　. . . Thousands of elderly patients have been transferred
from State mental institutions to nursing homes. The number
of aged in State mental hospitals decreased 40% between
1969 and 1973, according to subcommittee data, dropping
from 133,264 to 81,912. This trend is caused partially by progressive thinking intended to reduce patient populations in
large impersonal institutions. Another powerful reason, however, may be cost and the desire to substitute Federal for
State dollars. It costs the States an average of $800 per patient
per month to care for mental patients in State hospitals, while
these same individuals can be placed in boarding homes at a
substantially reduced cost. Charges of "wholesale dumping"
of patients have been made in several States. Acute problems
have been reported, most notably in California, Illinois, and
New York.

Supporting Paper No. 8 — "Access to Nursing Homes by U.S. Minorities"

. . . Only 4% of the 1 million nursing home patients in the United States are members of minority groups, even though their health needs are proportionately greater. Part of the problem is caused by cost obstacles or lack of information about Medicaid. Discrimination is the greatest obstacle to greater utilization by blacks. But discrimination need not be overt; often relatives are made to feel that their parents or grandparents would not be made comfortable. In the case of Asian Americans and Spanish-speaking Americans, language barriers often cause insurmountable difficulties. Cultural and other problems, including rural isolation, cause problems to American Indians. . . . Members of minority groups at sub-committee hearings have been sharply critical of the Nixon administration's nursing home "reforms." They protested the "arbitrary and punitive" closing of a few minority owned nursing homes that do exist and the absence of assistance to help upgrade standards.

Supporting Paper No. 9 — "Profits and the Nursing Home: Incentives in Favor of Poor Care"

. . . Profits by nursing homes have occasioned serious and persistent controversy. Nursing home administrators say that Medicaid reimbursement rates are low and that they can hardly become the basis for profiteering. Critics say that the economics of nursing home operation, supported in such large measure by public funds, should be examined more closely and publicly than they are now. . . . On the basis of available evidence, including a subcommittee survey made in 1973-74, the subcommittee has found that the 106 publicly held corporations controlled 18% of the industry's beds and accounted for one-third of the industry's $3.2 billion in revenue (as of 1972). Between 1969 and 1972, these corporations experienced the following growth:

    122.6% in total assets;
    149.5% in gross revenues; and
    116% in average net income.

One recent HEW study, however, shows marginal rates of return in a sample of 228 nursing homes. Thus, the issue is far from settled. But a joint study — conducted by the General

Accounting Office and the subcommittee — suggests significant increases in total assets, revenues, and profits for individual operators as well.

Two final documents will be issued as part of this study: A compendium of statements by the industry and administration spokesmen, and a final report by the Subcommittee on Long-Term Care.

General Conclusions

There is every reason to believe that the need for high quality long-term care facilities will continue to increase. One of the major reasons is that more and more people are living longer and longer. Individuals with multiple disabilities and advanced age are likely candidates for institutionalization. Any interpretation of these facts inevitably concludes that the thousands of seniors needing nursing home care but suffering at home will multiply rapidly in future years, unless significant changes in present practices are made.

It is time also for the Congress and the executive branch to improve the quality of life for the 1 million Americans presently residing in U.S. long-term care facilities. It is time, then, for the Congress and the executive branch to create a comprehensive national policy with respect to treatment of the infirm elderly.

It is time for providers of care to rise above mere public relations campaigns and join with senior citizens' spokesmen and Government officials in working for more positive improvements.

It is time that nursing homes began realizing their full potential as full and legitimate partners in the American health care system.

notes

Chapter 1

1. Robert Kastenbaum, "The Four Percent Fallacy," presented to the 1972 Annual Meeting of the Gerontological Society," printed in *Aging and Human Development*, 4, 1 (1973).

2. *Nursing Home Care in the United States: Failure in Public Policy.* "Introductory Report," prepared by the Subcommittee on Long-Term Care of the Special Committee on Aging, U.S. Senate (Washington, D.C.: Government Printing Office, December 1974), p. iii.

3. Ibid., p. 20

4. Ibid.

5. *The New York Times*, January 8, 1975.

6. *Nursing Home Care in the United States: Failure in Public Policy.* Supporting Paper No. 1, "The Litany of Nursing Home Abuses and an Examination of the Roots of Controversy," p. 199.

Chapter 3

1. Donald K. Ross, *A Public Citizen's Action Manual* (New York: Grossman, 1973), pp. 193-197.

2. Much of the information in this section was obtained from *Tactical Investigations for People's Struggles*, by Barry Greever, privately printed, September 1972; copies available from the Midwest Academy, 600 West Fullerton Avenue, Chicago, Illinois 60614.